# READ ME OUT LOUD!

## A Poem To Rap, Chant, Whisper
## Or Shout For Every Day Of The Year

### ...okson

Paul has been writing and editing books since he was eighteen and is one of the busiest poets you are likely to encounter. Always in demand with his performances and workshops, he has edited over twenty collections in the last ten years. He is also a lifelong Everton and Slade fan. Paul lives in Retford with his wife, Sally, and two children, Sam and Daisy.

### *Nick Toczek*

Nick goes swimming and buys things on eBay. He's a poet, magician, storyteller, puppeteer, novelist, comedian, local radio DJ and bald dad and grandad. He likes living in Bradford because he was born there. You can find lots more about him on the Internet. Try putting his name into a good search engine such as Google.

# READ ME OUT LOUD!

A Poem To Rap,
Chant, Whisper Or Shout
For Every Day Of The Year

Chosen by Paul Cookson
and Nick Toczek

MACMILLAN CHILDREN'S BOOKS

*For their editorial assistance in the final selection of the poems
included in this anthology, Nick Toczek and Paul Cookson would like to
thank Karen Cawthraw and Jemma Akers*

First published 2007 by Macmillan Children's Books
a division of Macmillan Publishers Limited
20 New Wharf Road, London N1 9RR
Basingstoke and Oxford
Associated companies throughout the world
www.panmacmillan.com

ISBN 978-0-330-44621-1

5 7 9 8 6 4

A CIP catalogue record for this book is available from
the British Library.

Typeset by Intype Libra Limited
Printed and bound in the UK by CPI Mackays, Chatham ME5 8TD

# Contents

# Contents

## February

# Contents

## March

# Contents

## April

# Contents

# Contents

## May

# Contents

# Contents

## July

# Contents

## August

# Contents

# Contents

## September

# Contents

## October

# Contents

## November

# Contents

# Contents

## December

# Contents

# *Read Me Out Loud – Introduction*

Read me . . . because I'm a book. Out loud . . . because that's how poetry began. And it's where much of our poetry still has its beginnings. And this selection of poems is particularly suited to being spoken, chanted, acted, sung and performed. With each poem, then, you'll have to choose the 'out loud' style that best suits the poem and your personality and your type of voice. There's no one right or wrong way. How you do it is your decision, so experiment. Try different reading styles and ways of using your voice. Do try to read with expression. Think about how the poet might have meant it to be read. Adjust your voice to suit the mood of the poem. A sad voice is very different from a happy one. And think about how loud or quiet you should be, and how fast or slow. It's all part of the enjoyment of poetry.

Remember too that poems like these *should* be read aloud. Poetry stems from an oral tradition. It's grown out of songs and story-telling, and out of the natural tones and rhythms of our everyday language. It's also rooted in the noises we find around us. One poem may, for example, echo the melody of a birdsong, while another might copy the rhythmic lapping of waves. Poems rock babies to sleep. Poems may contain the sound of a train or the rhythm of an axe. Poems celebrate luck and happiness, love and success, laughter and silliness. Poems moan about unfairness or loss. Poems express all your inner thoughts and reveal your secrets. Poems celebrate births and marriages. They vent anger. And poems remember those who have died. Poems contain everything in our lives. And these ones are for every day of your life. Lift them off the page. Rediscover and reinterpret them. Explore and experiment with the sound of the words, the music of the words, the rhythm and the expression. Forget what they look like on the paper. Concentrate on what you can make them sound like out loud. Your job is to feel them, sound them, breathe life into them. That's what this book is about.

So, have fun with these poems. Whether words from the distant past or words from the present, take the time to get to know them. Repeat them, learn them, feel their rhythms and release them.

This book is now yours. These poems are yours . . . so do whatever you like with them, as long as you do it out loud!

*Paul Cookson and Nick Toczek*

# January

## The Newcomer

Don't make a whisper –
    don't make a sound –
poor old Last Year's
    gone to ground.
Snoozing and snorting,
    he won't come back
though the icicles crinkle
    and the high wires crack.

Listen a moment . . .
    can you hear
something delicate
    drawing near,
little and faint
    and far away?
Those are the steps
    of New Year's Day.

New Year's bright with gold.
    He wears
bells on his ankles,
    rings on his ears –
whistles and dances
    and taps his drum.
Run and put the kettle on –
    NEW YEAR's
        COME!

*Jean Kenward*

## To *a* Poet *a* Thousand Years Hence

I who am dead a thousand years,
    And wrote this sweet archaic song,
Send you my words for messengers
    The way I shall not pass along.

I care not if you bridge the seas,
    Or ride secure the cruel sky,
Or build consummate palaces
    Of metal or of masonry.

But have you wine and music still,
    And statues and a bright-eyed love,
And foolish thoughts of good and ill,
    And prayers to them who sit above?

How shall we conquer? Like a wind
    That falls at eve our fancies blow,
And old Mæonides the blind
    Said it three thousand years ago.

O friend unseen, unborn, unknown,
    Student of our sweet English tongue,
Read out my words at night, alone:
    I was a poet, I was young.

Since I can never see your face,
    And never shake you by the hand,
I send my soul through time and space
    To greet you. You will understand.

*James Elroy Flecker*

## What's that? What's that

| Child 1 | What's an echo? |
|---------|-----------------|
| Child 2 | What's an echo? |

| Class | *I don't know.* |
|-------|-----------------|
|       | *I don't know.* |

| Child 1 | Is it fast or |
|---------|---------------|
| Child 2 | Is it fast or |
| Child 1 | Is it slow? |
| Child 2 | Is it slow? |

| Class | *I don't know.* |
|-------|-----------------|
|       | *I don't know.* |

| Child 1 | Is it scary? |
|---------|--------------|
| Child 2 | Is it scary? |

| Class | *I don't know.* |
|-------|-----------------|
|       | *I don't know.* |

| Child 1 | Close your eyes and |
|---------|---------------------|
| Child 2 | Close your eyes and |
| Child 1 | Make it go. |
| Child 2 | Make it go. |

| Child 1 | Did it? |
|---------|---------|
| *Class* | *No!* |
| Child 2 | Did it? |
| *Class* | *No!* |

| Child 1 | Can you throw it |
|---------|------------------|
| Child 2 | Can you throw it |
| Child 1 | Like a ball? |
| Child 2 | Like a ball? |

| *Class* | *I don't know* |
|---------|----------------|
|         | *I don't know* |

| Child 1 | Would it bounce back |
|---------|----------------------|
| Child 2 | Would it bounce back |
| Child 1 | Off a wall? |
| Child 2 | Off a wall? |

| *Class* | *Maybe so* |
|---------|------------|
|         | *Maybe so* |

| Child 1 | How will we know |
|---------|------------------|
| Child 2 | How will we know |
| Child 1 | When it's here? |
| Child 2 | When it's here? |

| *Class* | *I don't know* |
|---------|----------------|
|         | *I don't know* |

| | |
|---|---|
| Child 1 | How will we know |
| Child 2 | How will we know |
| Child 1 | When it's gone? |
| Child 2 | (Puts hands over mouth) |
| | |
| Child 1 | What's an echo? |
| Child 2 | (Keeps hands over mouth) |
| | |
| **Class** | *Now I know* |
| | *Now I know* |

*Roger Dunn*

# The Months

January brings the snow,
Makes our feet and fingers glow.

February brings the rain,
Thaws the frozen lake again.

March brings breezes loud and shrill,
Stirs the dancing daffodil.

April brings the primrose sweet,
Scatters daisies at our feet.

May brings flocks of pretty lambs,
Skipping by their fleecy dams.

June brings tulips, lilies, roses,
Fills the children's hands with posies.

Hot July brings cooling showers,
Apricots and gillyflowers.

August brings the sheaves of corn,
Then the harvest home is borne.

Warm September brings the fruit,
Sportsmen then begin to shoot.

Fresh October brings the pheasant,
Then to gather nuts is pleasant.

Dull November brings the blast,
Then the leaves are whirling fast.

Chill December brings the sleet,
Blazing fire, and Christmas treat.

*Sara Coleridge*

## *Advice for Spacemen*

When you test your rocket,
Oil the engine sprocket
You can't replace
In outer space.
Shops up there don't stock it.

When you fly your rocket,
Time your flight and clock it.
Don't exceed
Hyperspeed.
Safety first. Don't mock it.

When you park your rocket,
Do watch where you dock it.
The Spaceway Code
Says: off the road.
Otherwise, you block it.

When you mend your rocket,
Don't hammer it or knock it.
Just read the rules
On robot tools.
Then plug them in the socket.

When you leave your rocket,
Don't forget to lock it.
The only place
For keys in space
Is in your trouser pocket.

*Nick Toczek*

**6**

## *The Camels' Complaint*

All that way without a drink,
Night and day without a drink,
Sometimes freezing, sometimes hot,
Off in search of who knows what?

Left outside, we never saw
What our journey had been for.
We became bad-tempered then.
Who's to blame? Those three wise men!

*Sue Cowling*

## Monday's Child

Monday's child is fair of face,
Tuesday's child is full of grace,
Wednesday's child is full of woe,
Thursday's child has far to go,
Friday's child is loving and giving,
Saturday's child works hard for a living,
But the child that is born on the Sabbath day
is bonny and blithe and good and gay.

*Anon.*

## There Was an Old Man with a Beard

There was an Old Man with a beard,
Who said, 'It is just as I feared! –
    Two Owls and a Hen,
    Four Larks and a Wren,
Have all built their nests in my beard!'

*Edward Lear*

**9**

# The King of All the Dinosaurs

With taloned feet and razor claws,
Leathery scales, monstrous jaws . . .
The king of all the dinosaurs
Tyrannosaurus rex.

With sabre teeth no one ignores,
It rants and raves and royally roars . . .
The king of all the dinosaurs
Tyrannosaurus rex.

The largest of the carnivores,
It stomps and chomps on forest floors . . .
The king of all the dinosaurs
Tyrannosaurus rex.

Charges forward, waging wars,
Gouges, gorges, gashes, gores . . .
The king of all the dinosaurs
Tyrannosaurus rex.

With taloned feet and razor claws,
Leathery scales, monstrous jaws,
Sabre teeth no one ignores,
It rants and raves and royally roars . . .
The king of all the dinosaurs
Tyrannosaurus rex.

*Paul Cookson*

## *Team Talk*

'My team's better than your team.
We've got the best goal-getter.'

'If you think that, you're in a dream.
I'm telling you: my team's better.'

'My team's spending millions
On a really brilliant goalie.'

'Well, my team's spending squillions
On an Italian called Ravioli.'

'We've got the best supporters
And our manager's a world beater.'

'Your centre-forward's a tortoise.
Ours is as fast as a cheetah.'

'I think he needs specs to find the goal:
I've seen him miss from a foot.'

'Yours is hopeless at ball control.
Does he play with both eyes shut?'

'Rubbish! He's got very tricky feet.
I've seen him get goals galore.'

'Hey, what about when our teams meet . . . ?'

'I think it might be a draw.'

*Eric Finney*

**11**

# I Like Words

I like words.
Do you like words?
Words aren't hard to find:
Words on walls and words in books,
Words deep in your mind.

Words in jokes
That make you laugh,
Words that seem to smell.
Words that end up inside out,
Words you cannot spell.

Words that fly
And words that crawl,
Words that screech and bump.
Words that glide and words that swing,
Words that bounce and jump.

Words that paint
And words that draw,
Words that make you grin.
Words that make you shake and sweat,
Words that touch your skin.

Words of love
That keep you warm,
Words that make you glad.
Words that hit you, words that hurt,
Words that make you sad.

Words in French
And words in slang,
Words like 'guy' and 'dude'.
Words you make up, words you steal,
Words they say are rude.

I like words.
Do you like words?
Words come out and play.
Words are free and words are friends,
Words are great to say.

*Steve Turner*

## *Monsters*

Big heads
Big feet
Big hands
Big seat
Monsters!

Sharp teeth
Sharp nails
Sharp ears
Sharp tails
Monsters!

With scales
With wings
With horns
With stings
Monsters!

And moles
And warts
And stinks
And snorts
Monsters!

Some mean
Some mad
Some kind
Some sad
Monsters!

*Philip Waddell*

**13**

## *Sing a Song of Sixpence*

Sing a song of sixpence,
    A pocket full of rye;
Four and twenty blackbirds,
    Baked in a pie.

When the pie was opened,
    The birds began to sing;
Wasn't that a dainty dish,
    To set before the king?

The king was in his counting-house,
    Counting out his money;
The queen was in the parlour,
    Eating bread and honey.

The maid was in the garden,
    Hanging out the clothes.
When down came a blackbird,
    And pecked off her nose.

As it fell upon the ground,
    'Twas spied by Jenny Wren,
Who took a stick of sealing wax
    And stuck it on again.

*Anon.*

## *Wrapping Tutankhamun*

Tutankhamun's dead! Long live the King!
Let's get on down to the mummifying.
He may be dead, but he's looking well,
we pickled him in natron so that he don't smell.
Are his insides out? Has his body been stuffed?
Then let's get wrapping. We've checked enough.

18

*Go under 'n' over, criss-cross that strapping.*
*Keep overlapping. C'mon! Get wrapping!*

He wasn't very bright when alive, so it's said,
but he hasn't got a brain in his head now he's dead.
We dragged it through his nostrils with a long thin hook –
it showed us how to do it in our mummy's picture book.
If he's gonna live for ever, we don't want no mishaps,
so c'mon everybody, let's get him under wraps.

*Go under 'n' over, criss-cross that strapping.*
*Keep overlapping. C'mon! Get wrapping!*

Put a scarab where his heart was. Yeah, that's terrific,
is his name written on it in hieroglyphics?
That about wraps it up. He sure looks neat
from the top of his head to the soles of his feet.
We're wrapping Tutankhamun for the future to see,
so let's get wrapping for eternity.

*Go under 'n' over, criss-cross that strapping*
*Keep overlapping. C'mon! Get wrapping!*

*Jane Clarke*

# What Am I?
### *(Here's a fistful of clues)*

Help lender
Mail sender
Warm greeter
Card cheater
Yawn hider
Pen guider
Gift taker
Sign maker
Door knocker
Jaw socker
Tight gripper
Ear clipper
Five scorer
Explorer!

*Philip Waddell*

Answer: a hand

**16**

# A Wolf in the Park

Is there a wolf,
A wolf in the park,
A wolf who wakes when the night gets dark?
Is there a wolf in the park?

Is there a wolf,
A wolf who creeps
From his hidden den while the city sleeps?
Is there a wolf in the park?

Is there a wolf
Whose nightly track
Circles the park fence, zigzags back?
Is there a wolf in the park?

Is there a wolf
Who pads his way
Between the tables of the closed cafe,
Is there a wolf in the park?

Is there a wolf,
A wolf whose bite
Left those feathers by the pond last night,
Is there a wolf in the park?

Is there a wolf?
No one knows,
But I've heard a howl when the full moon glows . . .
Is there a wolf in the park?

*Richard Edwards*

## The Lightmare

'Are you sure there are no people?'
Sobbed the poltergeist in fright,
'I'm certain that I saw some
In the room downstairs last light –
The room below our attic
Where you told me not to go,
I fear I disobeyed you, mum
And crept there tippy toe.

I'm afraid I made a racket
When I tried to get away
And sent the tea set flying
And the table with the tray.
Then, scared out of my wits,
I tripped and bashed the dinner bell –
That's when the horrid people
Began to shriek and yell!

To get out of their way I leaped
A mighty leap in fear,
And in my blinding panic
Grabbed the crystal chandelier –
I didn't mean to smash it,
Just to swing and let them pass –
But the thing crashed to the ground
And showered them in glass!

I tell you, mum, it's *horrible* –
A screaming human face,
But when I tried to flee again
I bumped into the case,
It wobbled first a little
Then TIMBERED like a tree
And books flew out like startled birds
And hurled themselves through me!

I prayed I might awaken
For I could take no more,
That's when I saw, direct above,
Our little attic door.
Oh hold me, mum, and wail to me
A haunting lullaby –
I'll *never* disobey again –
However long I die!'

Said mum calmly, to comfort him,
'You shouldn't listen, son
To that silly Bogeyman –
Your dad's just having fun.
There are no horrid people –
Come let me dry your tears.
I told your dad his stories
Would make you have lightmares!'

*Philip Waddell*

## *A Small Dragon*

I've found a small dragon in the woodshed.
Think it must have come from deep inside a forest
because it's damp and green and leaves
are still reflecting in its eyes.

I fed it on many things, tried grass,
the roots of stars, hazel-nut and dandelion,
but it stared up at me as if to say, I need
foods you can't provide.

It made a nest among the coal,
not unlike a bird's but larger,
it is out of place here
and is quite silent.

If you believed in it I would come
hurrying to your house to let you share my wonder,
but I want instead to see
if you yourself will pass this way.

*Brian Patten*

## A Frog He Would a-Wooing Go

A frog he would a-wooing go,
  *Heigho, says Rowley,*
Whether his mother would let him or no.
With a rowley, powley, gammon and spinach,
  *Heigho, says Anthony Rowley!*

So off he sets in his opera hat,
  *Heigho, says Rowley,*
And on the road he met with a rat.
With a rowley, powley, gammon and spinach,
  *Heigho, says Anthony Rowley!*

'Pray, Mr Rat, will you go with me,'
  *Heigho, says Rowley,*
'Kind Mrs Mousey for to see?'
With a rowley, powley, gammon and spinach,
  *Heigho, says Anthony Rowley!*

When they came to the door of Mousey's Hall,
  *Heigho, says Rowley,*
They gave a loud knock, and they gave a loud call.
With a rowley, powley, gammon and spinach,
  *Heigho, says Anthony Rowley!*

'Pray, Mrs Mouse, are you within?'
  *Heigho, says Rowley,*
'Oh yes, kind sirs, I'm sitting to spin.'
With a rowley, powley, gammon and spinach,
  *Heigho, says Anthony Rowley!*

'Pray, Mrs Mouse, will you give us some beer?'
  *Heigho, says Rowley,*
'For Froggy and I are fond of good cheer.'
With a rowley, powley, gammon and spinach,
  *Heigho, says Anthony Rowley!*

'Pray, Mr Frog, will you give us a song?'
  *Heigho, says Rowley,*
'But let it be something that's not very long.'
With a rowley, powley, gammon and spinach,
  *Heigho, says Anthony Rowley!*

But while they were all a-merry-making,
  *Heigho, says Rowley,*
A cat and her kittens came tumbling in.
With a rowley, powley, gammon and spinach,
  *Heigho, says Anthony Rowley!*

The cat she seized the rat by the crown;
  *Heigho, says Rowley,*
The kittens they pulled the little mouse down.
With a rowley, powley, gammon and spinach,
  *Heigho, says Anthony Rowley!*

This put Mr Frog in a terrible fright,
   *Heigho, says Rowley,*
He took up his hat, and wished them goodnight.
With a rowley, powley, gammon and spinach,
   *Heigho, says Anthony Rowley!*

But as Froggy was crossing over a brook,
   *Heigho, says Rowley,*
A lily-white duck came and swallowed him up.
With a rowley, powley, gammon and spinach,
   *Heigho, says Anthony Rowley!*

*Anon.*

# Questions

What can you see
over the garden wall?

It all depends on whether you're
short or tall.

And when you're not looking
is what you saw still there?

The pictures inside your head
are everywhere.

What colour is the night
when you're fast asleep?

No colour and every colour,
dark and deep.

And what sound does a tree make
if no one hears it fall?

Every sound you've ever heard,
and no sound at all.


*Tony Charles*

**21**

## *Fairy Names*

What shall we call the Fairy Child?

Mouse-Fur? Cat's Purr?
Weasel-Wild?

Bat-Wing? Bee-Sting?
Shining River?
Snakebite? Starlight?
Stone? Or Shiver?

Acorn? Frogspawn?
Golden Tree?
Snowflake? Daybreak?
Stormy Sea?

Snail-Shell? Harebell?
Scarlet Flame?

How shall we choose the Fairy's name?

*Clare Bevan*

# As, as, as . . .

As slow as a start
as stopped as a heart
as thin as a chip
as chapped as a lip
as dour as a door
as high as the floor
as far as away
as near as today
as dreamy as far
as tall as a star
as dark as a lock
as stopped as a clock
as slow as a hiss
as near as a miss
as slim as an 'i'
as puzzled as 'y'
as warm as a purr
as boring as sir
as boring as sir
as boring as sir
as scrunched as a list
as white as a fist
as bold as a blizzard

as old as a wizard
as sad as the sea
as fit as a flea
as sick as our cat
as yukky as that
as slow as an end
as there as a friend
as quick as a kiss
as finished as this.

*Robert Hull*

# *All the world's a stage*

All the world's a stage,
And all the men and women merely players:
They have their exits and their entrances;
And one man in his time plays many parts,
His acts being seven ages. At first the infant,
Mewling and puking in the nurse's arms.
And then the whining schoolboy, with his satchel,
And shining morning face, creeping like snail
Unwillingly to school. And then the lover,

Sighing like furnace, with a woeful ballad
Made to his mistress' eyebrow. Then a soldier,
Full of strange oaths, and bearded like the pard,
Jealous in honour, sudden and quick in quarrel,
Seeking the bubble reputation
Even in the cannon's mouth. And then the justice,
In fair round belly with good capon lin'd,
With eyes severe, and beard of formal cut,
Full of wise saws and modern instances;
And so he plays his part. The sixth age shifts
Into the lean and slipper'd pantaloon,
With spectacles on nose and pouch on side,
His youthful hose well sav'd, a world too wide
For his shrunk shank; and his big manly voice,
Turning again toward childish treble, pipes
And whistles in his sound. Last scene of all,
That ends this strange eventful history,
Is second childishness and mere oblivion,
Sans teeth, sans eyes, sans taste, sans everything.

*William Shakespeare*

**24**

## *March Time: Dance Time*

One two three four, one two three four,
Left right, left right, stamp your feet.
One two three four, one two three four,
We go marching down the street.

One two three four, one two three four,
Swing your arms and breathe in deep.
One two three four, one two three four,
Up the hill however steep.

One two three four, one two three four,
Hold your head up, look your best.
One two three four, one two three four,
Soon be home and have a rest.

One two three four, one two three four,
Plod, plod . . . plod . . . plod. Feet like lead.
One two three four, one two three four,
All we want is to go to bed.

But –

*One two three, one two three, one two three, one two three,*
That's what we do when we skip.
*One two three, one two three, one two three, one two three,*
Leap in the air and don't slip.

*One two three, one two three, one two three, one two three,*
Tired? Never. Now we can fly.
*One two three, one two three, one two three, one two three,*
Up we go, ever so high.

*One two three, one two three, one two three, one two three,*
Out we go dancing to play.
*One two three, one two three, one two three, one two three,*
Iced-lolly-nice holiday.

*One two three, one two three, one two three, one two three,*
Mum's carried us up to bed.
*One two three, one two three, one two three, one two three,*
Dancing goes on in my head.

One two three, one two three, one two three, one two
three,
Dreaming, we hop, skip, and leap.
One two three, one two three, one two three, one two
three,
Mum whispers, 'Shh! They're asleep.'

*Leo Aylen*

## Seasons

In Springtime when the leaves are young,
Clear dewdrops gleam like jewels, hung
On boughs the fair birds roost among.

When Summer comes with sweet unrest,
Birds weary of their mother's breast,
And look abroad and leave the nest.

In Autumn ere the waters freeze,
The swallows fly across the seas: –
If we could fly away with these!

In Winter when the birds are gone,
The sun himself looks starved and wan,
And starved the snow he shines upon.

*Christina Rossetti*

# The Best Soundtrack Album in the World – Ever!

Your body, my body,
    everybody's got a body.
*Anybody, everybody,
    everyone has got a body.*

Hubble, bubble, hiccup, grumble,
splish, splosh, snuffle, squelch,
thud, glug, murmur, mumble,
whimper, whisper, rattle, belch.

Snort, snore, bubble, gurgle,
talk, squawk, snigger, sigh,
click, tick, hammer, burble,
rustle, whistle, yawn and cry.

Clap, tap, snap, slap, mutter,
grind, grunt, rumble, slurp,
huff, puff, blather, splutter,
gabble, babble, boo-hoo, burp.

Moan, groan, bellow, sniffle,
ring, sing, gasp and wheeze,
wail, whine, witter, whiffle,
thump, bump, beat and sneeze.

Giggle, guggle, babble, clatter,
sniff, scrape, tremble, squeak,
creak, snuffle, chuckle, chatter,
pitter-patter, chortle . . . speak.

*Your body, my body,*
   *everybody's got a body.*
*Anybody, everybody,*
   *everyone has got a body.*

*David Horner*

## *Night Mail*

This is the night mail crossing the border,
Bringing the cheque and the postal order,
Letters for the rich, letters for the poor,
The shop at the corner and the girl next door.
Pulling up Beattock, a steady climb –
The gradient's against her, but she's on time.
Past cotton grass and moorland boulder
Shovelling white steam over her shoulder,
Snorting noisily as she passes
Silent miles of wind-bent grasses.
Birds turn their heads as she approaches,
Stare from the bushes at her blank-faced coaches.
Sheepdogs cannot turn her course,
They slumber on with paws across.
In the farm she passes no one wakes,
But the jug in the bedroom gently shakes.

Dawn freshens, the climb is done.
Down towards Glasgow she descends
Towards the steam tugs yelping down the glade of cranes,
Towards the fields of apparatus, the furnaces
Set on the dark plain like gigantic chessmen.
All Scotland waits for her:
In the dark glens, beside the pale-green lochs
Men long for news.

Letters of thanks, letters from banks,
Letters of joy from girl and boy,
Receipted bills and invitations
To inspect new stock or visit relations,
And applications for situations
And timid lovers' declarations
And gossip, gossip from all the nations,
News circumstantial, news financial.
Letters with holiday snaps to enlarge in,
Letters with faces scrawled in the margin,
Letters from uncles, cousins and aunts,
Letters to Scotland from the South of France,
Letters of condolence to Highlands and Lowlands,
Notes from overseas to Hebrides –
Written on paper of every hue,
The pink, the violet, the white and the blue,
The chatty, the catty, the boring, adoring,
The cold and official and the heart's outpouring,
Clever, stupid, short and long,
The typed and the printed and the spelt all wrong.
Thousands are still asleep

Dreaming of terrifying monsters,
Of a friendly tea beside the band at Cranston's or
  Crawford's:
Asleep in working Glasgow, asleep in well-set Edinburgh,
Asleep in granite Aberdeen.
They continue their dreams;
But shall wake soon and long for letters,
And none will hear the postman's knock
Without a quickening of the heart,
For who can hear and feel himself forgotten?

*W. H. Auden*

## *The Day We Built the Snowman*

Round and round the garden
Rolling up the snow
One step, two step,
Watch the snowman grow.

Round and round the garden
Us and dad and mum,
Building up the snowman
Having lots of fun.

Mum has got a carrot,
Dad has got a pipe,
Sister's got a scarf
To keep him warm at night.

Baseball cap and shades,
Trainers for his feet,
Our trendy friendly snowman,
The coolest in the street.

Round and round the garden
In the winter weather,
The day we built the snowman . . .
Having fun together

Round and round the garden
Rolling up the snow
One step, two step,
Watch the snowman grow.

Round and round the garden
Us and dad and mum,
Building up the snowman
Having lots of fun.

*Paul Cookson*

# *What a Racket!*

Once upon a time,
We lived in a house in town
And
THE CATS MIAOWED,
THE DOGS BOW-WOWED,
THE COLD WIND HOWLED,
THE LORRIES ROARED,
THE AIRCRAFT SOARED,
THE WINDOWS RATTLED
AND THE THUNDER CRASHED.

'The trouble with living in *town*,' said Mum,
'is that it is SO noisy.'
So we moved to the country –
And
THE CATS MIAOWED,
THE DOGS BOW-WOWED,
THE SHEEP WENT BAA,
THE COWS WENT MOO,
THE TRACTORS CHUGGED,
THE COLD WIND BLEW,
THE THUNDER CRASHED,
THE FIELD MICE SQUEAKED,
THE RAIN POURED DOWN,
THE HOUSE ROOF LEAKED.

'Lovely!' said Mum.
'There's nothing quite like *country* sounds!'

*Trevor Harvey*

## The Hunter

I prowl across the patio,
A hunter in the dark.
As silent as a shadow,
Much meaner than a shark.

I creep around my kingdom,
I yearn to scratch and bite.
To hiss and howl and disembowel,
I'm master of the night!

Until . . . Oh help! Please, not that sound!
The only thing I fear!
*'Come on Fluffy! Come on puss!*
*Get yourself back 'ere!'*

*Ian Moore*

# Creative Writing

My story on Monday began:
*Mountainous seas crashed on the cliffs,*
*And the desolate land grew wetter . . .*
The teacher wrote a little note: *Remember the capital*
letter!

My poem on Tuesday began:
*Red tongues of fire*
*Licked higher and higher*
*From smoking Etna's top . . .*
The teacher wrote a little note: *Where is your full stop?*

My story on Wednesday began:
*Through the lonely, pine-scented wood*
*There twists a hidden path . . .*
The teacher wrote a little note: *Start a paragraph!*

My poem on Thursday began:
*The trembling child,*
*Eyes dark and wild,*
*Frozen 'midst the fighting . . .*
The teacher wrote a little note: *Take care untidy*
writing!

My story on Friday began:
  *The boxer bruised and bloody lay,*
  *His eye half closed and swollen*
The teacher wrote a little note: *Use a semi-colon!*

Next Monday my story will begin:
  *Once upon a time . . .*

Gervase Phinn

# *February*

## *People Ask*

My father travelled from Ceylon
Island of cinnamon and rubies
To my mother's birthplace
In the heart of Yorkshire

People ask
Where do you come from?
I say:
From more places
Than you imagine
My father's memories
My mother's dreams
Mines of gems and coal
Mango sunsets over rhubarb fields

People ask
Which half of you is white?
I say:
There are no halves in me
Everything is whole
I am a myriad of mingling
Multicoloured stories
Whispering wisely down
Through centuries

People ask
Where do you belong?
I say:
In the world
In my father's hopes
In my mother's songs
Most of all
In the place inside myself
Shining with its own futures

*Seni Seneviratne*

# The Jumping Game

We jump the rope
We jump in line
We jump up high
We jump in time
We jump for luck
We jump again
We jump along
The jumping game.

We jump in ones
We jump in twos
We jump the lights
We jump the queues
We jump for joy
We jump again
We jump along
The jumping game.

We jump and fall
We jump and learn
We jump and twist
We jump and turn
We jump for kicks
We jump again
We jump along
The jumping game.

We jump for gold
We jump for free
We jump from A
We jump to B
We jump for fun
We jump again
We jump along
The jumping game.

*Steve Turner*

## One Wicked Weasel

One wicked weasel with a cold in his nose.
Two trendy tigers tiptoeing on their toes.

Three thirsty thrushes nesting in a box.
Four furry foxes looking for their socks.

Five friendly field mice talking on the phone.
Six stripy snakes slithering over a stone.

Seven silly scorpions sitting in the sun.
Eight hungry elephants fighting for a bun.

Nine noisy nightingales singing in the dark.
Ten tired tortoises dozing in the park.

Eleven elegant emus exercising on the floor.
Twelve tricky turtles toppling through the door.

Thirteen tiny termites tripping over their feet.
Fourteen frenzied bull-frogs fainting in the heat.

Fifteen frozen fruit-bats hiding in the fridge.
Sixteen silky swans swimming by the bridge.

Seventeen spotted sea-lions diving in the sea.
Eighteen electric eels switching off for tea.

Nineteen naughty night-owls screeching in the trees.
Twenty tickly terrapins scratching around for fleas.

*Moira Andrew*

## My Locker

My locker's filled with lots of things
like feathers from a falcon's wings,
a basketball, a model plane,
a whistle from a railroad train,
a flower pot, a crystal dish,
a magazine with sharks and fish,
a roller skate, a pack of gum,
and cymbals from a drummer's drum.
It also has a boogie board,
a watergun, a plastic sword,
a handle for an ice cream scoop,
a thermos filled with chicken soup,
a pogo stick, a purple kite,
a lantern with an orange light,
a jar of nuts, a garden hose,
and tissues for my stuffy nose.

Although there's room for screws and hooks,
I have no place to put my books!

*Darren Sardelli*

# The Tyger

Tyger! Tyger! burning bright
In the forests of the night,
What immortal hand or eye
Could frame thy fearful symmetry?

In what distant deeps or skies
Burnt the fire of thine eyes?
On what wings dare he aspire?
What the hand dare seize the fire?

And what shoulder, and what art,
Could twist the sinews of thy heart?
And when thy heart began to beat,
What dread hand? and what dread feet?

What the hammer? what the chain?
In what furnace was thy brain?
What the anvil? what dread grasp
Dare its deadly terrors clasp?

When the stars threw down their spears,
And water'd heaven with their tears,
Did he smile his work to see?
Did he who made the Lamb make thee?

Tyger! Tyger! burning bright
In the forests of the night,
What immortal hand or eye
Dare frame thy fearful symmetry?

*William Blake*

**6**

## *Once Bittern*

The double-bass boom of the bittern,
Once common across much of Britain,
Is now seldom heard.
This endangered bird's
As rare as a poem well written.

*Nick Toczek*

## Five Little Speckled Frogs

Five little speckled frogs
Sat on a speckled log
Eating the most delicious bugs –
Yum, yum.
One jumped into the pool
Where it was nice and cool,
Then there were four green speckled frogs.
Glub, glub!

*Verses*
Four little speckled frogs, *etc.*
Three little speckled frogs, *etc.*
Two little speckled frogs, *etc.*

One little speckled frog
Sat on a speckled log
Eating the most delicious bugs –
Yum, yum.
He jumped into the pool
Where it was nice and cool,
Now there are no green speckled frogs.
Glub, glub!

*Anon.*

## *Cake-Face*

I like chocolate
cake, I like birthday
cake, I like ginger
cake, I like sponge
cake, I like fruit
cake, I like Christmas
cake, I like carrot
cake, I just can't stand
      stoma
cake.

*David Horner*

## *Tanka*

A letter from home
wafts in the smell of sand
in the monsoon rains –
dusk falls and I hear the peal
of temple bells in the wind . . .

*Usha Kishore*

## *The Star*

Twinkle, twinkle, little star,
How I wonder what you are!
Up above the world so high,
Like a diamond in the sky.

When the blazing sun is gone,
When he nothing shines upon,
Then you show your little light,
Twinkle, twinkle, all the night.

Then the traveller in the dark
Thanks you for your tiny spark,
He could not see which way to go,
If you did not twinkle so.

In the dark blue sky you keep,
And often through my curtains peep,
For you never shut your eye,
Till the sun is in the sky.

As your bright and tiny spark
Lights the traveller in the dark –
Though I know not what you are,
Twinkle, twinkle, little star.

*Jane Taylor*

## *Where Did We Go?*

We bought a ticket to . . . Kalamazoo
we went by train
by boat, by plane
around the world
and back again
through night and day
through sun and rain
through mist and snow . . .

Then where did we go?

We bought a ticket to . . . Timbuktu
*we went by train*
*by boat by plane* . . .

Then where did we go?

We bought a ticket to . . . Katmandu
*we went by train*
*by boat by plane* . . .

Then where did we go?

We bought a ticket to . . . Waterloo
*we went by train*
*by boat by plane . . .*

Then where did we go?

We bought a ticket to [you choose some places!]
*we went by train*
*by boat by plane . . .*

[last verse]
Then where did we go?
We bought a ticket to . . . Kalamazoo
    to Timbuktu
    to Katmandu
    to Waterloo
    to [your places!]
we went by train
by boat, by plane
around the world
and back again
through night and day
through sun and rain
through mist and snow . . .

Then where did we go?

Home
sweet
home!!!

*James Carter*

## Solomon Grundy

Solomon Grundy
Born on a Monday,
Christened on Tuesday,
Married on Wednesday,
Took ill on Thursday,
Worse on Friday,
Died on Saturday,
Buried on Sunday.
That was the end
Of Solomon Grundy.

*Anon.*

## City Centre Saturday

Car horns hooting,
Taxis tooting,
Motorbikes roaring,
Lorries snoring,
Sirens moaning,
Dustcarts groaning,
Bike wheels whipping,
Skateboards zipping,
Buskers singing,
Mobiles ringing,
Rock groups slamming,
Audience cramming,
Shoppers dashing,
Swing doors crashing,
Toddlers screeching,
Parents preaching,
Children whining,
Lost dogs pining.

First stars showing
Bus queues growing
Everyone going
Home

*Kate Williams*

## Sonnet 116

Let me not to the marriage of true minds
Admit impediments. Love is not love
Which alters when it alteration finds,
Or bends with the remover to remove:
O, no! it is an ever-fixèd mark,
That looks on tempests and is never shaken;
It is the star to every wandering bark,
Whose worth's unknown, although his height be taken.
Love's not Time's fool, though rosy lips and cheeks
Within his bending sickle's compass come;
Love alters not with his brief hours and weeks,
But bears it out even to the edge of doom.
   If this be error and upon me proved,
    I never writ, nor no man ever loved.

*William Shakespeare*

## *A Birthday*

My heart is like a singing bird,
  Whose nest is in a watered shoot;
My heart is like an apple-tree
  Whose boughs are bent with thick-set fruit;
My heart is like a rainbow shell
  That paddles in a halcyon sea;
My heart is gladder than all these
  Because my love is come to me.

Raise me a dais of silk and down;
  Hang it with vair and purple dyes;
Carve it in doves and pomegranates,
  And peacocks with a hundred eyes;
Work it in gold and silver grapes,
  In leaves and silver fleurs-de-lys;
Because the birthday of my life
  Is come, my love is come to me.

*Christina Rossetti*

# The Great Escape

In the Great Escape from London Zoo
Eight caribou and a gnu they knew
Mounted a minor military coup,
An act of animal derring-do,
And locked the staff they overthrew
In the 'potamus pit and a Portaloo,
Then caught a plane to North Peru.

As animals broke out two-by-two
To squeal and growl and grunt and moo
A loud unruly queue soon grew
That wriggled and ran and crawled and flew,
Stampeding down the avenue.

In the Great Escape from London Zoo
We heard how the herd of kangaroo
Had bid the big brown owl adieu
with a: 'Toodle-oo, mate, toodle-oo!'
But before he'd time to twit-tu-woo
They'd hopped it, heading for Timbuktu,
And the owl himself had flown off too.

While a crocodile and a cockatoo
Crossed the Thames in a slim canoe,
Rowed by the bird so the croc could chew . . .
Chew through the bones of the eight-man crew
Till the river ran red instead of blue.

In the Great Escape from London Zoo
The pandas abandoned their bamboo
And, all dressed up as railway crew,
Hijacked the fifteen fifty-two
From platform three at Waterloo
And, 'parley-voo', they zoomed straight through
Paris, and on to Katmandu.

Panic ensued and ballyhoo
When pot-bellied pig and rare-breed ewe
Gatecrashed a very posh barbecue
Terribly upsetting the well-to-do
And causing a heck of a hullabaloo.

You doubt my word? What's wrong with you?
Why, every detail here is true.
The Great Escape from London Zoo.
When was that? I thought you knew:
Years ago, at half past two.

*Nick Toczek*

## Winter Song

When will the winter end, Mother?
  When the grizzly's had its rest.
When will the grizzly wake, Mother?
  When the eider builds its nest.
When will the eider build, Mother?
  When the tundra starts to move.
When will the moving start, Mother?
  When the snow falls out of love.
When will the snowfall stop, Mother?
  When it finds new southern friends.
When will these friends be found, Mother?
  When the freezing winter ends.

*Linda Lee Welch*

## *Louder*

OK, Andrew, nice and clearly
off you go

Welcome everybody to our school concert . . .

Louder, please, Andrew.
Mums and dads won't hear you at the back, will they?

Welcome everybody to our school concert . . .

Louder, Andrew. You're not trying.
Pro –
      ject –
            your –
                  voice.

Take a  b i g  b r e a t h  and louder!

Welcome everybody to our school concert . . .

For goodness sake, Andrew. LOUDER! LOUDER!

# Welcome everybody to our school concert

Now, Andrew, there's no need to be silly.

*Roger Stevens*

# I Wrote Me a Poem

I wrote me a poem, and the poem pleased me.
I told my poem to the big oak tree.
My poem went: 'Fiddle-eye-dee'.

I wrote me a sonnet, and the sonnet pleased me.
I told my sonnet to the big oak tree.
My sonnet went: 'Ooh, love!' *(action: do a loud kiss)*
*My poem went: 'Fiddle-eye-dee'.*

I wrote me an ode, and the ode pleased me.
I told my ode to the big oak tree.
My ode went: 'Lah . . . dah'.
*My sonnet went: 'Oooh, love!' (loud kiss)*
*My poem went: 'Fiddle-eye-dee'.*

I wrote me an epic, and the epic pleased me.
I told my epic to the big oak tree.
My epic went: 'Too long, much too long'. *(stretch out arms)*
*My ode went: 'Lah . . . dah'.*
*My sonnet went: 'Oooh, love!' (loud kiss)*
*My poem went: 'Fiddle-eye-dee'.*

I wrote me a verse, and the verse pleased me.
I told my verse to the big oak tree.
My verse went: 'Tickety-boo, tickety-boo'.
*My epic went: 'Too long, much too long'. (stretch out
   arms)*
*My ode went: 'Lah . . . dah'.*
*My sonnet went: 'Oooh, love!' (loud kiss)*
*My poem went: 'Fiddle-eye-dee'.*

I wrote me a haiku and the haiku pleased me.
I told my haiku to the big oak tree.
My haiku went: 'Slooooow thought'.
*My verse went: 'Tickety-boo, tickety-boo'.*
*My epic went: 'Too long, much too long'. (stretch out
   arms)*
*My ode went: 'Lah . . . dah'.*
*My sonnet went: 'Oooh, love!' (loud kiss)*
*My poem went: 'Fiddle-eye-dee'.*

I wrote me a rhyme and the rhyme pleased me.
I told my rhyme to the big oak tree.
My rhyme went: 'Sky high'. *(stretch arms upwards)*
*My haiku went: 'Slooooow thought'.*
*My verse went: 'Tickety-boo, tickety-boo'.*
*My epic went: 'Too long, much too long'. (stretch out
   arms)*
*My ode went: 'Lah . . . dah'.*
*My sonnet went: 'Oooh, love!' (loud kiss)*
*My poem went: 'Fiddle-eye-dee'.*

I wrote me a limerick and the limerick pleased me.
I told my limerick to the big oak tree.
My limerick went: 'Silly-billy'. *(wag finger)*
*My rhyme went: 'Sky high'. (stretch arms upwards)*
*My haiku went: 'Slooooow thought'.*
*My verse went: 'Tickety-boo, tickety-boo'.*
*My epic went: 'Too long, much too long'. (stretch out arms)*
*My ode went: 'Lah . . . dah'.*
*My sonnet went: 'Oooh, love!' (loud kiss)*
*My poem went: 'Fiddle-eye-dee'.*

I wrote me a song and the song pleased me.
I told my song to the big oak tree.
My song went: 'Tree Shanty'.
*My limerick went: 'Silly-billy'. (wag finger)*
*My rhyme went: 'Sky high'. (stretch arms upwards)*
*My haiku went: 'Slooooow thought'.*
*My verse went: 'Tickety-boo, tickety-boo'.*
*My epic went: 'Too long, much too long'. (stretch out arms)*
*My ode went: 'Lah . . . dah'.*
*My sonnet went: 'Oooh, love!' (loud kiss)*
*My poem went: 'Fiddle-eye-dee'.*

I wrote me some words and the words pleased me.
I told my words to the big oak tree.
My words went: 'Jibber-jabber'.
*My song went: 'Tree Shanty'.*
*My limerick went: 'Silly-billy'. (wag finger)*

*My rhyme went: 'Sky high'. (stretch arms upwards)*
*My haiku went: 'Slooooow thought'.*
*My verse went: 'Tickety-boo, tickety-boo'.*
*My epic went: 'Too long, much too long'. (stretch out*
   *arms)*
*My ode went: 'Lah . . . dah'.*
*My sonnet went: 'Oooh, love!' (loud kiss)*
*My poem went: 'Fiddle-eye-dee'.*

*Bruce Barnes*

## *Unfinished Poem*

Here is the tiny seed.
Drop it from your palm.
Cover it with earth.

Here is the tender shoot
breaking through warm soil.
Water it with love.

Here is the slender stalk
Moist with morning dew.
Shelter it with care.

Here is the velvet bud
folded in itself.
See its slow unfurling.

Here is the fragrant flower
Open to the bees.
Watch their happy visiting.

Here is the shrivelled pod
rattling in cold wind.
Wait for the shell to split.

Here is the tiny seed.

*Barrie Wade*

## *New Day*

The day is so new
You can hear it yawning,
Listen:

The new day
is yawning
and stretching

and waiting to start.

In the clear blue sky
I hear the new day's heart.

*Ian McMillan*

## *The Faery Earl*

Oh, who is this comes ridin',
  Ridin' down the glen?
Is it one of our own Red-Branch Knights
  Or one of the King's men?

With feathers on his helmet,
  And gold upon his shield,
His horse is shod with silver shoes,
  He ridin' through the field!

Oh, this is not a Red-Branch
  Nor one of the King's men,
But this is faery Desmond
  Come ridin' back again.

'O lady of the Castle,
  O lady with gold hair,
O lady with eyes of pity,
  Come down the grey tower stair.

'For I may ask a question,
  And you may answer me,
When the sun is red in the forest,
  And the moon is white on the sea.'

Says she, 'Sir, ask your question,
   And I will answer you;
At sunset or at moonrise
   God send that I speak true!

'I know you by your helmet,
   And by your voice so sweet,
And by your coal-black charger
   With silver on his feet.

'God send you, faery Desmond,
   To come back to your own.'
Says he, 'Your answer, lady,
   Before the sun goes down.

'I'm ridin' ever and ever
   Over the land and sea;
My horse's shoes of silver,
   How long will they last me?'

The lady stood and pondered,
   The salt tear in her eye –
'Oh, would that I had magic
   To make a wise reply.

'Oh, will they wear forever,
   Or will they wear out fast?
Will he ride home this even'
   And stable his horse at last?'

'Sweet lady, quick, your answer!'
　'Now, God, what can I say? –
Those silver shoes will last, sir,
　To ride till Judgement Day.'


He turned, that faery horseman,
　And shook his bridle rein;
'Now, come the Day of Judgement
　Ere I ride home again.'


The sun went down in the forest,
　The moon shone bright as pearl,
The lady lay in the castle,
　And died for the faery Earl.


And ye will see him ridin',
　Ridin' down the glen
Over the seas and the rivers,
　Over the hill and the plain.


Ye'll see the plume on his helmet
　Waftin' among the trees,
And the silver shoes of his charger
　Chasin' the moonlit seas.


He's ridin' ever and ever,
　He'll ride till Judgement Day;
Oh, when that ride is over,
　May he ride home, we pray!


*Rosa Mulholland*

## Soldier, Soldier, Will You Marry Me?

Oh soldier, soldier, will you marry me,
With your musket, fife, and drum?
Oh no, pretty maid, I cannot marry you,
For I have no coat to put on.

Then off she went to the tailor's shop
As fast as legs could run,
And bought him one of the very very best
And the soldier put it on.

Oh soldier, soldier, will you marry me,
With your musket, fife, and drum?
Oh no, pretty maid, I cannot marry you,
For I have no socks to put on.

Then off she went to the sock-maker's shop
As fast as legs could run,
And bought him a pair of the very very best,
And the soldier put them on.

Oh soldier, soldier, will you marry me,
With your musket, fife, and drum?
Oh no, pretty maid, I cannot marry you,
For I have no shoes to put on.

Then off she went to the cobbler's shop
As fast as legs could run,
And bought him a pair of the very very best,
And the soldier put them on.

Oh soldier, soldier, will you marry me,
With your musket, fife, and drum?
Oh no, pretty maid, I cannot marry you,
For I have no hat to put on.

Then off she went to the hatter's shop
As fast as legs could run,
And bought him one of the very very best,
And the soldier put it on.

Oh soldier, soldier, will you marry me,
With your musket, fife, and drum?
Oh no, pretty maid, I cannot marry you,
For I have a wife at home.

*Anon.*

24

## *Poem for Sale*

Poem for sale
(One careful owner)
With simile,
(As lucky as a dime)
Two exquisite
And erudite adjectives
And one rhyme
Going
For a song

*Roger Stevens*

## The Cat of Cats

I am the cat of cats. I am
  The everlasting cat!
Cunning, and old, and sleek as jam,
  The everlasting cat!
I hunt the vermin in the night –
  The everlasting cat!
For I see best without the light –
  The everlasting cat!

*William Brighty Rands*

# The Enchanted Island

To Rathlin's Isle I chanced to sail,
    When summer breezes softly blew,
And there I heard so sweet a tale,
    That oft I wished it could be true.
They said, at eve, when rude winds sleep,
    And hushed is every turbid swell,
A mermaid rises from the deep,
    And sweetly tunes her magic shell.

And while she plays, rock, dell, and cave,
    In dying falls the sound retain,
As if some choral spirits gave
    Their aid to swell her witching strain.
Then summoned by that dulcet note,
    Uprising to th' admiring view,
A fairy island seems to float
    With tints of many a gorgeous hue.

And glittering fanes, and lofty towers,
    All on this fairy isle are seen;
And waving trees, and shady bowers,
    With more than mortal verdure green.
And as it moves, the western sky
    Glows with a thousand varying rays;
And the calm sea, tinged with each dye,
    Seems like a golden flood of blaze.

They also say, if earth or stone,
From verdant Erin's hallowed land,
Were on this magic island thrown,
Forever fixed, it then would stand.
But, when for this, some little boat
In silence ventures from the shore –
The mermaid sinks – hushed is the note,
The fairy isle is seen no more!

*Anon.*

## I Had a Little Horse

I had a little horse,
His name was Dappled Grey.
His head was made of gingerbread,
His tail was made of hay.
He could amble, he could trot,
He could carry the mustard pot,
He could amble, he could trot,
Through the old Town of Windsor.

*Anon.*

## World of Weird
*(groups of boys/girls do alternate verses)*

In the world of Weird
all the girls wear beards
and the boys keep bees in their beds
the girls dig holes and live like moles
and the boys grow trees on their heads

In the world of Weird
all the oranges are blue
and the lemons are as sweet as can be
bananas are round and grow in the ground
or down at the bottom of the sea

In the world of Weird
all the fish can fly
and the chips are fried in lakes
the dogs love cats: with sauce, of course –
served up on silver plates

Now how do you get
to the world of Weird? –
where is it? where is it? where?
hop on a bee – pop over the sea
then gives us a call when you're there!

*James Carter*

## *An Alphabet for the Planet*

A for air.
The gentle breeze by which we live.
B for bread.
A food to bake and take – and *give*.
C for climate.
It can be warm, it can be cold . . .
D for dolphin.
A smiling friend no net should hold.
E for Earth.
Our ship through space, and home to share.
F for family,
Which also means people *everywhere*.

G for green.
Colour of life we'll help to spread.
H for healthy.
Happy and strong, no fumes with lead.
I for ivory.
The elephant's tusks, his *own* to keep.
J for jungle.
A rainforest. No axe should creep.
K for kindly.
To everyone, gentle and good.
L for life.
It fills the sea and town and wood.
M for mother.
She may feel hurt, but loves us all.
N for nest.
A tiny home for chicks so small.
O for Ozone.
It shields our Earth from harmful rays.
P for peace.
'My happy dream,' the Planet says.
Q for quiet.
Where no loud noise can get at you.
R for recycled.
Old cans and cards as good as new.
S for Sun.
The nearest star. It gives us light.
T for tree.
A grander plant, a green delight.
U for united.
Working as one to put things right.

V for victory.
Winning over disease and war.
W for water.
The whole earth drinks when rainclouds pour.
X for Xylophone.
Music from wood – the high notes soar!
Y for yummy.
Those tasty fruits 'organically grown'.
Z for zoo.
A cage a condor – sad, alone.

*Riad Nourallah*

# *March*

## *A Change in the Year*

It is the first mild day in March:
    Each minute sweeter than before,
The redbreast sings from the tall larch
    That stands beside our door.

There is a blessing in the air,
    Which seems a sense of joy to yield
To the bare trees, and mountain bare,
    And grass in the green field.

*William Wordsworth*

## *spring*

Stealthily
pours
refreshment
into
neglected
ground

slinkily
persuades
roots
into
new
germination

serenely
promises
richnesses
if
nurtured
generously

sharp
points
reluctantly
inch
needled
green

sap
pushing
rhythms
inkily
now
grows

stems
proudly
radiating
indelible
nectary
gold

*Lynne Taylor*

## *The Browny Hen*

A browny hen sat on her nest
    With a hey-ho for the springtime!
Seven brown eggs 'neath her downy breast,
    With a hey-ho for the springtime!

A brown hen clucks all day from dawn,
    With a hey-ho for the springtime!
She's seven wee chicks as yellow as corn,
    With a hey-ho for the springtime!

*Irene F. Fawsey*

# Poem for Attracting Mum's Attention

**M**um
Mum
Mum
Mum
Mum
Mum
Mum
Mum
Mum
Mum
Mum
Mum

*Roger Stevens*

*Note: I know . . . it doesn't look like much of a poem, does it?*
*But try saying it out loud in a variety of voices.*

## *Daffodils*

I wander'd lonely as a cloud
 That floats on high o'er vales and hills,
When all at once I saw a crowd,
 A host of golden daffodils;
Beside the lake, beneath the trees,
Fluttering and dancing in the breeze.

Continuous as the stars that shine
 And twinkle on the Milky Way,
They stretch'd in never-ending line
 Along the margin of a bay:
Ten thousand saw I at a glance,
Tossing their heads in sprightly dance.

The waves beside them danced, but they
 Out-did the sparkling waves in glee:
A poet could not but be gay,
 In such a jocund company:
I gazed – and gazed – but little thought
What wealth the show to me had brought:

For oft, when on my couch I lie
   In vacant or in pensive mood,
They flash upon that inward eye
   Which is the bliss of solitude;
And then my heart with pleasure fills,
And dances with the daffodils.

                        *William Wordsworth*

## The Skin I'm In
### (a rap)

The skin I'm in
the skin I'm in
I'm feeling happy
with the skin I'm in

I never think
about fat or thin
I've got no problem
with the skin I'm in

those model girls
don't bother me
when I look at myself
I like what I see

I'm not impressed
by catwalk glamour
I'm feeling good
about who I am – a

girl who's fine in her skin
on cloud nine in her skin
celebrating
thinking straight and
feeling great in MY skin!

*Sue Cowling*

# The Moon

The moon has a face like the clock in the hall;
She shines on thieves on the garden wall,
On streets and fields and harbour quays,
And birdies asleep in the forks of the trees.

The squalling cat and the squeaking mouse,
The howling dog by the door of the house,
The bat that lies in bed at noon,
All love to be out by the light of the moon.

But all of the things that belong to the day
Cuddle to sleep to be out of her way;
And flowers and children close their eyes
Till up in the morning the sun shall arise.

*Robert Louis Stevenson*

## Where Teachers Keep Their Pets

Mrs Cox has a fox
Nesting in her sweaty socks.

Mr Spratt's tabby cat
Sleeps beneath his bobble hat.

Miss Cahoots has various newts
Swimming in her zip-up boots.

Mr Spry has Fred his fly
Eating food stains off his tie.

Mrs Groat shows off her stoat
Round the collar of her coat.

Mr Spare's got grizzly bears
Hiding in his spacious flares.

And . . .

Mrs Vickers . . . has a stick insect called Stickers
And she keeps it in her . . .

*Paul Cookson*

## I Had a Little Nut Tree

I had a little nut tree;
Nothing would it bear
But a silver nutmeg
And a golden pear;
The King of Spain's daughter
Came to visit me,
And all for the sake of
My little nut tree.
I skipped over water,
I danced over sea,
And all the birds in the air
Couldn't catch me.

*Anon.*

## *Ducking and Diving*
### *(Action)*

I'm practising ducking and diving
bobbing down and swerving like this
It's all with the aim of fooling Aunt Madge
in the hope I can cause her to miss
cos the first thing she'll do when she gets here today
is grab me and give me a kiss

Aaaaaaaghh!

*Susan Bates*

## The Cats of Kilkenny

There were once two cats of Kilkenny,
Each thought there was one cat too many;
So they fought and they fit,
And they scratched and they bit,
Till, excepting their nails
And the tips of their tails,
Instead of two cats, there weren't any.

*Anon.*

## Barrel-Organ Song

I'm a Czechoslovakian drowned sailor-man,
My name is Frantishek,
When I was alive, I whistled this song
As I swabbed the lower deck:

*O happy was I, happy was I, happy as can be,*
*With a maiden called Euphoria, sitting on my knee.*

Now I live with a mermaid beneath the waves,
A girl salty and sweet.
I'm her only dear darling of all the drowned
Czechoslovakian fleet.

*O happy am I, happy am I, happy as can be,*
*With a maiden called Euphoria, sitting on my knee.*

*Gerda Mayer*

## Monkey Motto

I leap through the trees.
I drop to the ground.
That's what I do –
*Monkey around.*

I pounce on my tail.
I bounce and I bound.
That's what I do –
*Monkey around.*

I spit out the pips
Of fruit I have found.
That's what I do –
*Monkey around.*

I hear my own hoots.
I shriek at the sound.
That's what I do –
*Monkey around.*

Want to have fun
That won't cost a pound
*Here's what you do –*
*Monkey around.*

*Clare Bevan*

*Note: a good excuse for actions and jungle noises.*

## *Danger Spots*

When in a country
With a climate
More than tepid-y

A jungle walk
Is well and good
If you're intrepid-y

Or in a party
Safely led
By someone shepherd-y

But should you spot
A spotted cat
Whose pelt is peppered-y

A large and loping
Streamlined feline
Looking leopard-y

That's heading your way
Relocate yourself
Quick-stepper-dy

Because to stay there's
To remain where
You're in jeopardy.

*Nick Toczek*

## Julius Caesar's Last Breakfast

I'm tired this morning
Off my food
Hardly touched the olives, lark or dormouse
We stayed out late last night
With Lepidus
And talked of death
Drank too much wine
And now Calpurnia, my wife,
Is in a mood
She dreamed a death
And it was mine.

I'm tired this morning
The winds of March
Are blowing like a hurricane
Through Rome
At the Pontifical Palace
The God of Mars crashed to the floor
And what that means, I'm not quite sure.

I'm tired this morning
Upon the Ides of March
The Senate can convene without me
Yes, I think I'll stay at home.

*Roger Stevens*

Note: *On the morning of Julius Caesar's assassination, the chamber at the Senate was full. But Caesar's chair was empty. He was nowhere to be found. The conspirators sent Marcus Brutus to Caesar's house to persuade him to attend.*

## *The Cow*

The friendly cow, all red and white,
I love with all my heart:
She gives me cream with all her might,
To eat with apple-tart.

She wanders lowing here and there,
And yet she cannot stray,
All in the pleasant open air,
The pleasant light of day;

And blown by all the winds that pass
And wet with all the showers,
She walks among the meadow grass
And eats the meadow flowers.

*Robert Louis Stevenson*

# Cloakroom Argument
*(Children 'argue' by contradicting each statement.)*

I'm taller than you.
*No you're not!*

I do more work than you.
*No you don't!*

You've got my pen.
*No I haven't!*

You broke my ruler.
*No I didn't!*
Did!
*Didn't!*
Did!
*Didn't!*
Did!
*Didn't!*

You should be outside.
*No I shouldn't!*

You're not as old as me.
*Yes I am!*

You haven't got your PE kit.
*Yes I have!*

You don't know what to do.
*Yes I do!*

You won't come on the school trip.
*Yes I will!*

You shouldn't be inside.
*Yes I should!*
Shouldn't!
*Should!*
Shouldn't!
*Should!*
Shouldn't!
*Should!*

You're always arguing.
*No I'm not!*

*Andy Seed*

## The Cherry Pie Song

'Will you chew a little quieter?' said the hippo to the bee.
'There's a bunch of gerbils up ahead I've invited round to
  tea.
How keen they'll be to wash their paws and eat our cherry
  pie.
They are waiting at the bus-stop with tear-drops in their
  eye.
Can they, can't they, can they, can't they eat some cherry
  pie?
Can they, can't they, can they, can't they eat some cherry
  pie?'

'It is quite delightful,' bee replied, 'to stand beside the weir
And listen to the frogspawn with a gherkin in your ear,
To munch away at cherry pie and hear the gerbils sing
The Hallelujah Chorus and do the Highland Fling.
Will they, won't they, will they, won't they do the Highland
  Fling?
Will they, won't they, will they, won't they, do the
  Highland Fling?'

'Of course they will,' the hippo said, 'and we'll all play
   rock guitars,
Drink tulip tea and daffodil squash and dance beneath the
   stars.
Fear not, my busy buzzing friend, chew up your currant
   bun,
Put your best boots on, dear bee, and join what will be
   fun.
Will you, won't you, will you, won't you join us in the
   fun?
Will you, won't you, will you, won't you join us in the
   fun?'

*Matt Simpson*

## We're The Downhill Racers

Pushing pedals, setting paces
Windblown hair and smiling faces
Grinning, winning speeding aces
We're the downhill racers

Great adventures, going places
Rocket ships to lunar bases
Motorcycle cops on chases
We're the downhill racers

Thrills and spills – faster faster!
Gliding wheels sliding past you
Hear the squeals and shouts of laughter
We're the downhill racers

Hi-octane adrenalin pumping
Hammer pounding, heartbeat thumping
Wild excited jumping, bumping
We're the downhill racers

Wheels of fire – we're fanatics
On cloud nine – we're ecstatic
Mad for it – we're cyclopathic
We're the downhill racers

The urge to surge downhill's appealing
Nothing else can beat this feeling
Leading, speeding and freewheeling
We're the downhill
                    downhill
                            racers!

*Paul Cookson*

## *He Just Can't Kick It with His Foot*

John Luke from our team
Is a goalscoring machine
Phenomenally mesmerizing but . . .
The sport is called football
But his boots don't play at all
Cos he just can't kick it with his foot

He can skim it from his shin
He can spin it on his chin
He can nod it in the net with his nut
He can blow it with his lips
Or skip it off his hips
But he just can't kick it with his foot

With simplicity and ease
He can use his knobbly knees
To blast it past the keeper, both eyes shut
He can whip and flick it
Up with his tongue and lick it
But he still can't kick it with his foot

Overshadowing the best
With the power from his chest
Like a rocket from a socket he can put
The ball into the sack
With a scorcher from his back
But he just can't kick it with his foot

Baffling belief
With the ball between his teeth
He can dribble his way out of any rut
Hypnotize it with his eyes
Keep it up on both his thighs
But he just can't kick it with his foot

From his shoulder to his nose
He can juggle it and pose
With precision and incision he can cut
Defences straight in half
With a volley from his calf
But he just can't kick it with his foot

He can keep it off the deck
Bounce the ball upon his neck
With his ball control you should see him strut
He can flap it with both ears
To loud applause and cheers
But he just can't kick it with his foot

He can trap it with his tum
Direct it with his bum
Deflect it just by wobbling his gut
When he's feeling silly
He can even use his . . . ankle!
But he just can't kick it with his foot!

*Paul Cookson*

## *Bodywork*

*Fibula, tibia, tarsals and rib,*
*clavicle, cranium, spine;*
*whatever the outside appearance,*
*all praise to the inner design!*

I've a mandible, patella, metatarsal,
I have biceps, I have triceps and a brain;
a pulmonary artery takes blood one way,
then back it comes through pulmonary vein.
There's retina and anvil, epiglottis,
oesophagus and pancreas and tongue;
how could I cope without my parathyroids,
Eustachian tube or diaphragm or lung?

*Fibula, tibia, tarsals and rib,*
*clavicle, cranium, spine;*
*whatever I seem from the outside,*
*you can't fault the inner design!*

*Judith Nicholls*

## Run

Foot pounding
Beat sounding
Gear shifting
Mood lifting
Blood pumping
Chest thumping
Sweat breaking
Breath taking
Rhythm beating
Body heating
Thoughts whirring
Engine purring
Lungs filling

Muscles thrilling
Skin zinging
Heart singing

*Jane Saddler*

# How to Successfully Persuade Your Parents to Give You More Pocket Money

Ask, request, demand, suggest, cajole or charm
Ingratiate, suck up to, flatter, compliment or smarm
Negotiate, debate, discuss, persuade, convince, explain
Or reason, justify, protest, object, dispute, complain
Propose, entreat, beseech, beg, plead, appeal, implore
Harass, go on about it, pester, whinge, whine, nag and bore
Annoy, insult, reproach, denounce, squeal, scream and
    shout
Go quiet, subdued, look worried, fret, brood, tremble,
    shiver, pout
Act depressed, downhearted, upset, snivel, sigh
Go all glum and plaintive, wobble bottom lip and cry
Sniff, sulk, grumble, stare at ceiling, mope, pine, stay in bed

Get cross, get angry, fume, seethe, fester, agitate, see red
Provoke, enrage, push, bully, aggravate and goad
Screech, smoke, burn up, ignite, spark, detonate, EXPLODE

And if all that doesn't work

Here are two little tricks
That should do it with ease

No. 1: smile
No. 2: say please.

*Andrea Shavick*

## from *The Eagle*

He clasps the crag with crooked hands;
Close to the sun in lonely lands,
Ring'd with the azure world, he stands.

The wrinkled sea beneath him crawls;
He watches from his mountain walls,
And like a thunderbolt he falls.

*Alfred, Lord Tennyson*

## Storms

My mum's afraid of thunderstorms
That sweep up from the sea.
As lightning cracks and thunder rolls
We share a mug of tea.
As window panes begin to shake
We like to watch TV.
My mum's afraid of thunderstorms
Except when she's with me.

*Ron Simmons*

## Fuss Fuss Fuss or The Goldilocks Rap

Hey everybody, listen, yo!
here's a tale you might just know
it's all about the 3 Bears 3
and the fussiest girl you ever did see
who went by the name of Little Miss G

Now G was out in the woods one day
when after a while she lost her way
and deeper and deeper into the wood
she followed the smell of something good

Soon she came to a dreamy cottage
and 3 hot bowls of creamy porridge –

*Fuss Fuss Fuss!*

one too lumpy, one too hot
but one just right – she scoffed the lot!

*Fuss Fuss Fuss!*

Next 3 chairs – and two weren't right
the other she broke – it served her right!

*Fuss Fuss Fuss!*

Next 3 beds, it was number 3
where G took a nap so peacefully

*Fuss Fuss Fuss!*

The bears came back before too long
crying 'What the ding dong's going on?!?'
and finding G in the tiny bed
It made those 3 Bears 3 see red

'Hey Goldie girl, you keep it real –
you can't just barge in here and steal
our food! – you go and cook some more
you lazybod – you know the score'

Never before in the dreamy cottage
had tastier bowls of creamy porridge
been cooked (by the bears or anyone)
so the bears said, 'G – it'd be such fun

to open a diner!' They did, it was cool
and G's food made those wood folk drool
and the fussiest girl you ever did see – went

*Fuss Fuss Fuss!*

well, no actually –

the fussiest girl you ever did see
cooked porridge – ever after – quite happily

*James Carter*

## Kidding Around

When I'm with Laura
　　I need to be loud;
When I'm with Paula
　　I always feel proud,
But when I'm with Carol
　　I'm one of the crowd.

When I'm with Kevin
　　I'm thoughtful and kind,
But when I'm with Michael
　　I'm out of my mind.

When I'm with Wanda
　　I want the last word;
When I'm with Bella
　　I sing like a bird:
And when I'm with Hector
　　I can hardly be heard.

But when I sit quietly
　　Under this tree,
That is the time
　　When I can be me.

*Dave Ward*

## *Tall Nettles*

Tall nettles cover up, as they have done
These many springs, the rusty harrow, the plough
Long worn out, and the roller made of stone:
Only the elm butt tops the nettles now.

This corner of the farmyard I like most:
As well as any bloom upon a flower
I like the dust on the nettles, never lost
Except to prove the sweetness of a shower.

*Edward Thomas*

# Pow!-*erful Sound Effects!*

*Pow!*
*Pop!*
*Zip!*
*Wham!*
*Zap!*
*Snap!*
*Snip!*
*Bam!*
*Boom!*
*Zoom!*
*Clap!*
*Clang!*
*Splash!*
*Crash!*
*Whack!*
*Bang!*
*Clank!*
*Clack!*
*Clink!*
*Zing!*

Great
Sounds
These
Bring!

*Robert Scotellaro*

## Garden Rhyme

One pot.
Two seeds.
Three flowers.
Four bees.
Five hives.
Six trees.
Seven branches.
Eight leaves.
Nine birds.
Ten nests.
Eleven worms.
Twelve pests.
Thirteen gardens.
Fourteen sheds.

Fifteen weeds in flower beds.
Sixteen rows of peas and beans.
Seventeen plots of spinach and greens.
Eighteen mowers.
Nineteen hoses.
Twenty greenfly on twenty roses.

*Phil Rampton*

## O Captain! My Captain!

O Captain! my Captain! Our fearful trip is done;
The ship has weathered every rack,
The prize we sought is won;
The port is near, the bells I hear,
The people all exulting,
While follow eyes the steady keel,
The vessel grim and daring;
   But O heart! heart! heart!
   O the bleeding drops of red,
   Where on the deck my Captain lies,
   Fallen cold and dead.

O Captain! my Captain! Rise up and hear the bells;
Rise up – for you the flag is flung,
For you the bugle trills:
For you bouquets and ribboned wreaths,
For you the shores a-crowding;
For you they call, the swaying mass,
Their eager faces turning;
  Here, Captain! dear father!
  This arm beneath your head;
  It is some dream that on the deck
  You've fallen cold and dead.

My Captain does not answer, his lips are pale and still;
My father does not feel my arm,
He has no pulse nor will,
The ship is anchored safe and sound,
Its voyage closed and done;
From fearful trip, the victor ship
Comes in with object won:
  Exult, O shores, and ring, O bells!
  But I, with mournful tread,
  Walk the deck my Captain lies,
  Fallen cold and dead.

*Walt Whitman*

# April

## This Little Poem

This little poem has five lines
and five words in every line.
I wrote it out five times
between five o'clock and five past nine
using five different pencils every time
and this little poem tells lies.

Ian McMillan

# Rain! Rain!

**R**ain!   *Rain!*
Sings the frog
To an empty sky
*Rain!*   *Rain!*
Sings the frog
Because the land is dry.

*Rain!*   *Rain!*
Sings the frog
And the West Wind starts to blow
*Rain!*   *Rain!*
Sings the frog
As pouting storm clouds grow.

*Rain!*   *Rain!*
Sings the frog
Dancing on webbed feet
*Rain!*   *Rain!*
Sings the frog
As thunder drums a beat.

Rain! Rain!
Sings the frog
And others join his call
Rain! Rain!
Sings the frog
As at last the raindrops fall.

*Kevin McCann*

## Home-thoughts, from Abroad

Oh, to be in England
Now that April's there,
And whoever wakes in England
Sees, some morning, unaware,
That the lowest boughs and the brushwood sheaf
Round the elm-tree bole are in tiny leaf,
While the chaffinch sings on the orchard bough
In England – now!

And after April, when May follows,
And the whitethroat builds, and all the swallows!
Hark, where my blossomed pear-tree in the hedge
Leans to the field and scatters on the clover
Blossoms and dewdrops – at the bent spray's edge –
That's the wise thrush; he sings each song twice over,
Lest you should think he never could recapture
The first fine careless rapture!
And though the fields look rough with hoary dew,
All will be gay when noontide wakes anew
The buttercups, the little children's dower
– Far brighter than this gaudy melon-flower!

*Robert Browning*

## The Caterpillar

Brown and furry
Caterpillar in a hurry,
Take your walk
To the shady leaf, or stalk,
Or what not,
Which may be the chosen spot.
No toad to spy you,
Hovering bird of prey pass by you;
Spin and die,
To live again a butterfly.

*Christina Rossetti*

## Old Noah's Ark

Old Noah once he built an ark,
And patched it up with hickory bark.
He anchored it to a great big rock,
And then he began to load up his stock.

The animals went in one by one,
The elephant chewing a carroway bun.

The animals went in two by two,
The crocodile and the kangaroo.

The animals went in three by three,
The tall giraffe and the tiny flea.

The animals went in four by four,
The hippopotamus stuck in the door.

The animals went in five by five,
The bees mistook the bear for a hive.

The animals went in six by six,
The monkey was up to his usual tricks.

The animals went in seven by seven,
Said the ant to the elephant, 'Who're ye shoving?'

The animals went in eight by eight,
Some were early and some were late.

The animals went in nine by nine,
They all formed fours and marched in line.

The animals went in ten by ten,
If you want any more, you can read it again.

*Anon.*

# I Asked the Little Boy Who Cannot See

I asked the little boy who cannot see,
'And what is colour like?'
'Why, green,' said he,
'Is like the rustle when the wind blows through
The forest; running water, that is blue;
And red is like a trumpet sound; and pink
Is like the smell of roses; and I think
That purple must be like a thunderstorm;
And yellow is like something soft and warm;
And white is a pleasant stillness when you lie
And dream.'

*Anon.*

## Pippa Passes

The year's at the spring,
And day's at the morn;
Morning's at seven;
The hillside's dew-pearled;
The lark's on the wing;
The snail's on the thorn;
God's in His Heaven –
All's right with the world.

*Robert Browning*

## And Did Those Feet in Ancient Time

And did those feet in ancient time
Walk upon England's mountains green?
And was the holy lamb of God
On England's pleasant pastures seen?

137

And did the countenance divine
Shine forth upon our clouded hills?
And was Jerusalem builded here
Among those dark satanic mills?

Bring me my bow of burning gold:
Bring me my arrows of desire:
Bring me my spear: O clouds unfold!
Bring me my chariot of fire.

I will not cease from mental fight,
Nor shall my sword sleep in my hand
Till we have built Jerusalem
In England's green and pleasant land.

*William Blake*

## Cross Your Fingers
### *(for Luck)*

Cross your fingers
Cross your palms
Cross your thumbs
Cross your arms

Cross your legs
Cross your toes
Cross your eyes
Cross your nose

Cross your head
Cross your heart
Cross your end
Cross your start

Cross your self
Cross the floor
Cross the carpet
Cross the door

Cross your father
Cross your mother
Cross your sister
Cross your brother

Cross your crosses
Cross your noughts
Cross your feelings
Cross your thoughts

Cross your grin
Cross your frown
Cross your road
Cross your town

Cross your where
Cross your why
Cross the ocean
Cross the sky

Cross your oohs
Cross your aahs
Cross the planets
Cross the stars

Cross this rhythm
Cross this rhyme
Cross all of space
And all of time . . .

Now,
Are you feeling lucky?

*David Bateman*

## *The First Bit*

I love the first bit of the morning,
The bit of the day that no one has used yet,
The part that is so clean
You must wipe your feet before you walk out into it.
The bit that smells like rose petals and cut grass
And dampens your clothes with dew.

If you go out you will bump into secrets,
Discover miracles usually covered by bus fumes.
You will hear pure echoes, whispers and scuttling.

I love the first bit of the morning
When the sun has only one eye open
And the day is like a clean shirt,
Uncreased and ready to put on;
The part that gets your attention
By being so quiet.

*Coral Rumble*

## Two Times Table

Twice one are two,
Violets white and blue.

Twice two are four,
Sunflowers at the door.

Twice three are six,
Sweet peas on their sticks.

Twice four are eight,
Poppies at the gate.

Twice five are ten,
Pansies bloom again.

Twice six are twelve,
Pinks for those who delve.

Twice seven are fourteen,
Flowers of the runner bean.

Twice eight are sixteen,
Clinging ivy ever green.

Twice nine are eighteen,
Purple thistles to be seen.

Twice ten are twenty,
Hollyhocks in plenty.

Twice eleven are twenty-two,
Daisies wet with morning dew.

Twice twelve are twenty-four,
Roses . . . who could ask for more.

*Anon.*

## James Bond Car

So this, you say, was James Bond's car
Did you get it from a dealer?
I love the feel of the steering wheel.
*Don't touch that lever!*

I love the colour – the go-faster stripes
The upholstery of leather
And nozzle for making oil skids.
*Don't touch that lever!*

An in-board computer with gadgets galore
Pours lemonade – if you need a breather –
And is this a rocket launcher? Wow!
*Don't touch that lever!*

I wish I had a James Bond car.
It's a real scene-stealer.
And look – it's got ejector seats.

*Don't touch that . . .*

# AAAAaaaaaaaaaahhhhhhhhhhhhhhhh

*Roger Stevens*

*(To be performed leaping from chair at end as though ejected. After the first reading everyone might like to join in the last line.)*

## *The Planets*

In the middle
is the Sun,

Then comes Mercury,
number one.

Venus next is number two,
and then a planet spinning blue:

The Earth, our home,
is number three.

Look through the stars,
what do we see?

Red desert Mars
is number four

Of all the planets,
then there's more.

Jupiter is number five,
after that we will arrive

At Saturn's rings
for number six.

Moving on
we quickly slip

To Uranus at number seven
out there in the misty heaven.

Then Neptune waits
at number eight:

So all the planets make a line
and Pluto's last at number nine!

*David Greygoose*

## How doth the little crocodile

How doth the little crocodile
    Improve his shining tail,
And pour the waters of the Nile
    On every golden scale!

How cheerfully he seems to grin,
    How neatly spreads his claws,
And welcomes little fishes in,
    With gently smiling jaws!

*Lewis Carroll*

## *Embryonic Mega-Stars*

We can play reggae music, funk and skiffle too,
We prefer heavy metal but the classics sometimes do.
We're keen on Tamla-Motown, folk and soul,
But most of all, what we like
Is basic rock and roll.
We can play the monochord, the heptachord and flute,
We're OK on the saxophone and think the glockenspiel is
    cute,
We really love the tuba, the balalaika and guitar
And our duets on the clavichord are bound to take us far.
We think castanets are smashing, harmonicas are fun,
And with the ocarina we have only just begun.
We've mastered synthesizers, bassoons and violins
As well as hurdy-gurdies, pan-pipes and mandolins.
The tom-tom and the tabor, the trumpet and the drum
We learnt to play in between the tintinnabulum.
We want to form a pop group
And will when we're eleven,
But at the moment Tracey's eight
And I am only seven.

*Brian Patten*

# There's a Bird That Comes Flying
### *(German folk song)*

There's a bird that comes flying,
settles down on my knee,
and he carries a letter
from my mother to me.

Little bird, take the greeting,
take a kiss and a tear,
for I cannot go with you,
as I have to stay here.

*Translated by Gerda Mayer*

## *Batman*

Batman
Age 10½
Patrols the streets of his suburb
At night
Between 7 and 8 o'clock.
If he is out later than this
he is spanked
and sent to bed
Without supper.

Batman
Almost 11
Patrols the streets of his suburb
At night
If he has finished his homework.

Batman,
His secret identity
And freckles
Protected
By the mask and cloak
His Auntie Elsie
Made on her sewing machine,
Patrols
At night
Righting Wrongs.

Tonight he is on the trail of
Raymond age 11
(large for his age)
Who has stolen Stephen's
Gobstoppers and football cards.

Batman
Patrolling the streets of his suburb
Righting Wrongs
Finds Raymond,
Demands the return of the stolen goods.
Raymond knocks him over.
Rips his mask,
Tears his cloak,
And steals his utility belt.
Batman starts to cry,
Wipes his eyes with his cape
(His hankie was in the belt).

Next day
Auntie Elsie says
This is the fourteenth time
I've had to mend your
Batman costume.
If it happens again
You'll have to whistle for it.

Batman
Eats a bag of crisps.

*John Turner*

151

# Chants

*(Sound each syllable as in a football chant)*

bacon
egg and beans,
toast and butter –
BREAKFAST!
*(English)*

croissants,
sliced baguette
coffee and jam –
BREAKFAST!
*(Continental)*

drip, drop,
drip, drop, drip,
drip, drop, drip, drip –
RAINFALL!

two teams,
stadium,
two sets of fans –
FOOTBALL!

presents,
roast turkey,
tinsel and tree –
CHRISTMAS!

olives,
anchovies,
tomato and cheese –
PIZZA!

lions,
elephants,
naughty monkeys
THE ZOO!

keyboard.
mouse and mat,
computer games –
PC!

candles,
cake and cards
party poppers –
BIRTHDAY!

do this,
don't do that,
pocket money –
PARENTS!

carrots
floppy ears,
hutches and straw –
RABBITS!

blue skies,
ice-cream vans,
seaside and sand –
SUMMER!

*Ray Mather*

## Transported to Australia

Transported to Australia,
A convict bound in chains,
Transported to Australia,
Through winds and storms and rains.

*Raging sea, raging sea,*
*I know you'll be the death of me.*

Transported to Australia –
I stole a loaf of bread,
Tired, hungry, racked with pain,
And more than halfway dead.

*Raging sea, raging sea,*
*I know you'll be the death of me.*

Transported to Australia
In eighteen twenty five,
Crying for my England home,
And only just alive.

*Raging sea, raging sea,*
*I know you'll be the death of me.*

Transported to Australia
With countless other men,
Thinking of the family
I'll never see again.

*Raging sea, raging sea,*
*I know you'll be the death of me.*

*Raging sea, raging sea,*
*Oh take me now and set me free.*

*Clive Webster*

# Let Me Hear You Say . . .

*(A repeat-after-me poem. Perform with a strong beat. You can even sing it if you like!)*

Let me hear you say, Wo-o-o-o-oh
*(everyone repeats)* **Wo-o-o-o-oh**
Yeah-e-e-e-ah
**Yeah-e-e-e-ah**
Wo-o-o-o-oh
**Wo-o-o-o-oh**
Yeah Yeah Yeah Yeah
**Yeah Yeah Yeah Yeah**
Wo oh-oh-oh YEAH!
**Wo oh-oh-oh YEAH!**
Doo doo doo doo di do-di dum
**Doo doo doo doo di do-di dum**
Doo-bi-doo-bi-diddy dah doo doo DAH!
**Doo-bi-doo-bi-diddy dah doo doo DAH!**
Zibbidi dibbidy dibby di doo doo WAH!
**Zibbidi dibbidy dibby di doo doo WAH!**
Niggle piggle giggle wriggle nicky nicky noo
**Niggle piggle giggle wriggle nicky nicky noo**
Blibby blobby gnick gnick quack quack quack
**Blibby blobby gnick gnick quack quack quack**
*(noise of diving plane)* Yeeeeeeeeeeeeaaaaaaaooooowwwww
**Yeeeeeeeeeeeeaaaaaaaooooowwwww**
I'm as daft as a parrot flying in a fridge

I'm as daft as a parrot flying in a fridge
OK everybody, you can stop right now
**OK everybody, you can stop right now**
*(loudly)* I said we've finished the poem you can stop right
now
**I said we've finished the poem you can stop right now!**
*(quieter)* We've finished the poem you can stop right now
**We've finished the poem you can stop right now**
*(very quiet)* We've finished the poem you can stop right now
**We've finished the poem you can stop right now**
*(very quiet indeed)* Shhhhhhhhhhhhhhhhhhhhhhhhhhhhhhh
**Shhhhhhhhhhhhhhhhhhhhhhhhhhhhhhhh**

*Roger Stevens*

## *Parents' Jobs*

My dad's a paramedic.
Nee naw nee naw nee naw nee naw.

My dad's a joiner.
Cut cut cut cut – hammer hammer – ouch!

My mum's a doctor.
Sit down
what's the matter?
Where does it hurt?

My mum's a teacher.
Sit up!
Calm down!
Put your lips together!

My dad's a dentist.
Open wide!
Let's look inside
Now does this hurt?
YESSSSS!!!!!!!

My dad's a chef.
Sizzle sizzle
Stir stir
bubble bubble – READY!

My mum drives a taxi.
Going far?
The roads are busy!
Tick . . . tick . . . tick . . . tick

Mum works in a shop.
Scan . . . scan . . . scan . . . scan
Can I have a packer, please?

My dad fixes cars.
(Sharp intake of breath)
Brrrum Brrrum Brrrum Brrrum
Splutter splutter – BANG!

My dad works in a factory.
Make it, check it, pack it, sell it!
Make it, check it, pack it, sell it!

My mum's a traffic warden.
You can't park here!
You can't park here!
I'll book you!
I'll clamp it!
You can't park here!

My mum's a librarian.
Shh Shh Shh Shh
Read it, read it, read it, read it,
Shh Shh Shh Shh

My dad's a bus driver.
Fares please!
Fares please!
Move to the end of the bus!

My dad's a builder.
Dig it, mix it, build it high!
Dig it, mix it, build it high!

*Lisa Watkinson*

## *Fleet Flight*

A flea met a fly in a flue,
Said the flea let us fly
Said the fly let us flee
So they flew through a flaw in the flue.

*Anon.*

# *George and the Dragon*

*T*here are two child actors, one dressed as St George, the other as a (not so fearsome) dragon.

*St George*
I am St George and I am here to fight the dragon.

      *The dragon (rather reluctantly)*
And I am the dragon and I suppose I have to fight St George.

*St George (pompously)*
I come to you from lands afar,
To rid you of this dreadful foe,
To kill the beast that all men fear,
And end this tale of woe.

         *The dragon*
  Why pick on me? I mean no harm,
  Although I do eat men and piglets,
  But, for me, they're only just a snack,
  They're nothing more than Twiglets.

*St George*
You lay waste the land with your fearful fire,
And cause many a poor man's death.
You burn our houses; you fry our crops;
And roast us with your fiery breath.

> *The dragon*
> A little burp, that's all it was!
> I hiccuped and burnt most of Surrey.
> I really must apologize,
> But it's worse when I've had a curry.

*St George*
To arms, Dragon. We fight!

*The dragon shrugs.*

*They fight.*

*St George keeps thrusting with his sword. The dragon deftly avoids him. Finally the dragon turns to the audience, looks thoroughly bored with the whole thing and gives St George an uppercut to the chin.*

*St George falls down, mortally wounded.*

*The dragon wins! He turns to the audience and clasps both hands above his head, as boxers do when they win.*

*St George (apparently dying)*
Well, that was a surprise and no mistake.

*Rob Falconer*

## *New Sights*

I like to see a thing I know
Has not been seen before,
That's why I cut my apple through
To look into the core.

It's nice to think, though many an eye
Has seen the ruddy skin,
Mine is the very first to spy
The five brown pips within.

*Anon.*

## *That's You and Me!*

As friends we:

whisper,
discuss,
argue
then float messages across a crowded playground
that only we know and understand.

As friends we:

walk,
stumble,
run
then spring after each other
so close we exchange shadows as we go.

As friends we:

laugh,
cry,
care
then taste each other's thoughts
and share each other's moods.

One girl, one boy,
one friendship to enjoy.
One lock, one key,
that's you and me!

*Ian Souter*

## *Counting Song*

**1** is a sword

**2** is a swan

**3** a fried worm

**4** a full sail and

**5** is the hook
I hang my coat on . . .

*Kevin McCann*

## *Some Salamanders*

Some salamanders say your name.
Some salamanders pray for fame.
Some salamanders slay and maim.

Some salamanders may show shame.
Some salamanders, they take aim.
Some salamanders sway when lame.

Some salamanders lay the blame.
Some salamanders pay that claim.
Some salamanders weigh the same.

Some salamanders play the game.
Some salamanders stay quite tame.
Some salamanders wade through flame.

*Nick Toczek*

## Sea-fever

I must go down to the seas again, to the lonely sea and the
sky,
And all I ask is a tall ship and a star to steer her by,
And the wheel's kick and the wind's song and the white
sail's shaking,
And a grey mist on the sea's face and a grey dawn
breaking.

I must go down to the seas again, for the call of the
running tide
Is a wild call and a clear call that may not be denied;
And all I ask is a windy day with the white clouds flying,
And the flung spray and the blown spume, and the sea-
gulls crying.

I must go down to the seas again, to the vagrant gypsy life,
To the gull's way and the whale's way where the wind's
like a whetted knife;
And all I ask is a merry yarn from a laughing fellow-rover,
And quiet sleep and a sweet dream when the long trick's
over.

*John Masefield*

# *What For!*

One more word from you, said my dad,
And I'll give you what for.

What for? I said.

That's right, he said, what for!

No, I said, I mean what for?
What will you give me what for for?

Never you mind, he said. Wait and see.

But what is what for for? I said.

What's what for for? he said.
It's to teach you what's what,
That's what.

What's that? I said.

Right, he said, you're for it,
I'm going to let you have it.

Have what? I said.

Have what? he said.
What for, that's what.
Do you want me to really give you
Something to think about?

I don't know, I said,
I'm thinking about it.

Then he clipped me over the ear.

It was the first time he'd made sense
All day.

*Noel Petty*

# *This Is the Key to the Castle*

This is the key to the castle

This is the box
with rusty locks
that holds the key to the castle

This is the spider, huge and fat,
who wove its web and sat and sat
on top of the box
with rusty locks
that holds the key to the castle

This is the cellar, cold and bare,
dark as the grave, with nobody there
except the spider, huge and fat,
who wove its web and sat and sat
on top of the box
with rusty locks
that holds the key to the castle

This is the stair that crumbles and creaks
where every small step moans and squeaks
that leads to the cellar, cold and bare,
dark as the grave, with nobody there

except the spider, huge and fat,
who wove its web and sat and sat
on top of the box
with rusty locks
that holds the key to the castle.

This is the rat with yellow teeth,
sharp as sorrow, long as grief,
who ran up the stair that crumbles and creaks
where every small step moans and squeaks
up from the cellar, cold and bare,
dark as the grave, with nobody there
except the spider, huge and fat,
who wove its web and sat and sat
on top of the box
with rusty locks
that holds the key to the castle

This is the damp and dirty hall
with peeling paper on its mouldy wall
where the black rat runs with yellow teeth
sharp as sorrow, long as grief,
who ran up the stair that crumbles and creaks
up from the cellar, cold and bare,
dark as the grave, with nobody there
except the spider, huge and fat,
who wove its web and sat and sat
on top of the box
with rusty locks
that holds the key to the castle

This is the ghost with rattling bones,
carrying his head, whose horrible groans
fill the damp and dirty hall
with peeling paper on its mouldy wall
where the black rat runs with yellow teeth
sharp as sorrow, long as grief,
who ran up the stair that crumbles and creaks
up from the cellar, cold and bare,
dark as the grave, with nobody there
except the spider, huge and fat,
who wove its web and sat and sat
on top of the box
with rusty locks
that holds the key to the castle

This is the child who came in to play
on a rainy, windy, nasty day
and said BOO! to the ghost who groaned in the hall
and SCAT! to the rat by the mouldy wall
and went down the creaking crumbling stair
into the cellar, cold and bare,
and laughed at the spider, huge and fat,
and brushed off the web where it sat and sat
and opened the box
with rusty locks
and took the key to the castle.

*Dave Calder*

# May

## Alliteration Rap

Sarah, with her satchel, skipping home from school,
Chanting out her lessons, feeling very cool.
Yesterday in literacy, she learnt a new technique;
Now *alliteration* dominates her week.

Sarah, with her satchel, starts another rhyme;
Loves how leading letters add a sense of time.
Working out the words and building up the beat,
Sarah skips along to the rhythm of the street.

Sarah, with her satchel and her new-found voice,
Croaks her new creations, overwhelmed by choice.
Double beats and triple beats come with every breath;
After mastering the method she's doing it to death!

Sarah, with her satchel, arrives at her front gate
But begins to notice the technique start to grate.
As lines of words get longer she finds them hard to say;
Thinks thankfully 'tis time to terminate today!

*Ray Mather*

## Missing Important Things

I didn't go to school this week
I stayed at home with Dad.
I didn't do a worksheet
and I am really rather glad.
I didn't do the number work,
I didn't do my words,
I didn't learn my spellings
and I didn't read my page.
I didn't go to school today –
we fixed the shed instead,
tied some flies and feathers
and dug the onion bed.
I saw the cat have kittens,
I climbed right up a tree,

mixed some sand and water
and held a bumblebee.
I didn't go to school all week
and I'm really not too sad –
I missed important lessons
and stayed at home with Dad.

*Peter Dixon*

## I Dreamed Last Night

I dreamed last night of dinosaurs
Way back in space and time,
In forest ferns and lush green trees,
A land of swamps and slime.

I saw a Diplodocus plod
With long extended neck.
He was as heavy as a bus
And left the plants a wreck.

I saw an Allosaurus grip
His prey with powerful claws.
Eleven metres long he was
With dagger teeth and jaws.

I saw an Ornithomimus.
An athlete, he could run
As fast as any modern horse
And mimic birds in fun.

I saw a huge Triceratops
With three defensive horns.
He charged with these at predators
And dug up trees and thorns.

But then I saw Tyrannos rex,
His eyes on me as prey.
Oh how I ran and was relieved
To wake to light of day!

*Jane Mann*

## Ariel's Song

Full fathom five thy father lies,
  Of his bones are coral made:
Those are pearls that were his eyes,
  Nothing of him that doth fade,
But doth suffer a sea-change
  Into something rich, and strange:
Sea-nymphs hourly ring his knell –
  Hark! now I hear them,
    *Ding-dong bell.*

*William Shakespeare*

## If All the World Were Paper

If all the world were paper,
And all the sea were inke;
And all the trees were bread and cheese,
What should we do for drinke?

*Anon.*

# The Cook's Tragedy

*(A Short Play for Ham Actors)*

A: I once knew a cook who moved among the cream of society.

B: A good egg?

A: Unfortunately he thought he could have his cake and eat it.

B: You mean he wanted everything on a plate?

A: Exactly. He thought life was going to be as easy as pie.

B: Obviously he never used his loaf.

A: One day, when the chips were down, he turned sour.

B: I suppose he became a fast liver?

A: He didn't give a sausage for anyone.

B: No doubt he ended up in the soup?

A: Of course. He realized his goose was cooked when he heard the police had a bone to pick with him.

B: You mean he was acting fishy and they grilled him?

A: He told them a half-baked story and they gave him a real roasting.

B: Such lives are food for thought.

*Brian Patten*

## You Are Special

You are more special than a sunrise
Or a mountain covered in snow;
You're more special than
the most important secret you could know.

You're more special than the winning goal
In the last minute of the match,
More wonderful than a winning serve
Or a fielder's diving catch.

You're more fantastic than a musical
That makes the whole world sing;
More special than a chocolate cake
With double-chocolate icing.

You're more important than the last panda
Or gorilla left on earth,
Than an eagle or a peacock;
Just see how much you're worth.

You are more beautiful than emeralds
More wonderful than gold,
You're more special than
the most exciting story ever told.

You're not an accident or a burden
Or a terrible mistake;
You're special,
You're original,
You're the best thing God could make.

*Chris Bambrough*

## *Cupboard Love*

*Apple pie and cider,*
*Who's afraid of spiders?*
*Sally caught the old grey mare,*
*But found she couldn't ride her.*
*She's got ribbons in her hair*
*Hanging down beside her.*
*Apple pie and cider*
*Who's afraid of spiders?*

Voice 1:    My spider's got nine legs,
Voice 2:    He lives in my pocket,
Voice 3:    He drinks cups of coffee,
Voice 4:    He eats purple parrots with mustard and
            toffee
Voice 5:    And washing lines and clothes pegs
Voice 6:    And butter beans and kedgeree,
Voice 7:    And basketballs and cricket bats.
Voice 8:    On summer evenings after tea,
            He goes outside and hunts for cats.

*Apple pie and cider,*
*Who's afraid of spiders?*
*Sally caught the old grey mare,*
*But found she couldn't ride her.*
*She's got ribbons in her hair*
*Hanging down beside her.*
*Apple pie and cider*
*Who's afraid of spiders?*

*Tony Charles*

## *Scarborough Fair*

Where are you going? To Scarborough Fair?
Parsley, sage, rosemary and thyme,
Remember me to a bonny lass there,
For once she was a true lover of mine.

Tell her to make me a cambric shirt,
Parsley, sage, rosemary and thyme,
Without any needle or thread work'd in it,
And she shall be a true lover of mine.

Tell her to wash it in yonder well,
Parsley, sage, rosemary and thyme,
Where water ne'er sprung nor a drop of rain fell,
And she shall be a true lover of mine.

Tell her to plough me an acre of land,
Parsley, sage, rosemary and thyme,
Between the sea and the salt sea strand,
And she shall be a true lover of mine.

Tell her to plough it with one ram's horn,
Parsley, sage, rosemary and thyme,
And sow it all over with one peppercorn,
And she shall be a true lover of mine.

Tell her to reap it with a sickle of leather,
Parsley, sage, rosemary and thyme,
And tie it all up with a tom tit's feather,
And she shall be a true lover of mine.

Tell her to gather it all in a sack,
Parsley, sage, rosemary and thyme,
And carry it home on a butterfly's back,
And then she shall be a true lover of mine.

*Anon.*

## *The Elephant*

An elephant's a wondrous thing
He trumpets but he doesn't sing;
His back is bigger than his front
I wish I were an elephant!

His feet are thick, his tail is thin
(I wonder what he has within?)
His trunk can do just what it wants
There's nothing quite like elephants!

His tusks stick down and up and out
His trunk could give you quite a clout;
His ears are bigger than a tent
There's nought to beat the elephant!

*Anthony Manville*

## A Word

A word is dead
When it is said,
Some say.

I say it just
Begins to live
That day.

*Emily Dickinson*

# The Song of the Mischievous Dog

There are many who say that a dog has its day,
  And a cat has a number of lives;
There are others who think that a lobster is pink,
  And that bees never work in their hives.
There are fewer, of course, who insist that a horse
  Has a horn and two humps on its head,
And a fellow who jests that a mare can build nests
  Is as rare as a donkey that's red.
Yet in spite of all this, I have moments of bliss,
  For I cherish a passion for bones,
And though doubtful of biscuit, I'm willing to risk it,
  And I love to chase rabbits and stones.
But my greatest delight is to take a good bite
  At a calf that is plump and delicious;
And if I indulge in a bite at a bulge,
  Let's hope you won't think me too vicious.

*Dylan Thomas*

## New Shoes

My shoes are new and squeaky shoes,
They're very shiny, creaky shoes,
I wish I had my leaky shoes
That Mother threw away.

I liked my old, brown, leaky shoes
Much better than these creaky shoes,
These shiny, creaky, squeaky shoes
I've got to wear today.

*Anon.*

## The Mystery

I am the wind which breathes upon the sea,
I am the wave of the ocean,
I am the murmur of the billows,
I am the ox of the seven combats,
I am the vulture upon the rocks,
I am a beam of the sun,
I am the fairest of plants,
I am the wild boar in valour,
I am a salmon in the water,
I am a lake in the plain,
I am a word of science,
I am the point of the lance of battle,
I am the God who created in the head the fire.
Who is it who throws light into the meeting on the
    mountain?
Who announces the ages of the moon?
Who teaches the place where couches the sun?

(If not I)

*Amergin*
*Translated by Douglas Hyde*

## A Red, Red Rose

O my love's like a red, red rose
That's newly sprung in June:
O my love's like the melodie
That's sweetly played in tune.

So fair art thou, my bonnie lass,
So deep in love am I;
And I will love thee still, my dear,
Till a' the seas gang dry.

Till a' the seas gang dry, my dear,
And the rocks melt wi' the sun;
I will love thee still, my dear,
While the sands o' life shall run.

And fare thee weel, my only love!
And fare thee weel a while!
And I will come again, my love,
Though it were ten thousand mile.

*Robert Burns*

## The Millennium Falcon

Okay
I know
You're right
It doesn't look much
A plastic tube
Metallic paint, some wood, some wire
But it's the Millennium Falcon
Spaceship for hire

It's been travelling the universe
For five years and a day
And it was built by granddad
Before he passed away

Okay
I know
You're right
It doesn't look much
Metallic paint, some wire, some wood
But it fought and beat the Empire
For the forces of good

And now, upon my bedroom shelf
It's found its final rest
I know it doesn't look much
But in its day it was the best

*Roger Stevens*

## Song of the Homeworkers

*This is effective read by a large group to a beaten-out rhythm which gradually increases in tempo. Alternatively, two groups can alternate the lines. Either way, this is essentially a group poem.*

Homework, moanwork, cross it out and groanwork
Homework, neat work, keeps you off the street work
Homework, moanwork, cross it out and groanwork
Homework, roughwork, when you've had enough work
Homework, moanwork, cross it out and groanwork
Homework, dronework, do it on you own work
Homework, moanwork, cross it out and groanwork
Homework, gloomwork, gaze around the room work
Homework, moanwork, cross it out and groanwork

Homework, guesswork, book is in a mess work
Homework, moanwork, cross it out and groanwork
Homework, rushwork, do it on the bus work
Homework, moanwork, cross it out and groanwork
Homework, hatework, hand your book in late work
Homework, moanwork! Cross it out and groan **groan
GROANWORK!**

*Trevor Millum*

## Cargoes

Quinquireme of Nineveh from distant Ophir
Rowing home to haven in sunny Palestine
With a cargo of ivory,
And apes and peacocks,
Sandalwood, cedarwood, and sweet white wine.

Stately Spanish galleon coming from the Isthmus,
Dipping through the Tropics by the palm-green shores,
With a cargo of diamonds,
Emeralds, amethysts,
Topazes, and cinnamon, and gold moidores.

Dirty British coaster with a salt-caked smoke stack
Butting through the Channel in the mad March days,
With a cargo of Tyne coal,
Road-rail, pig-lead,
Firewood, iron-ware, and cheap tin trays.

*John Masefield*

## *Body Talk*

Dere's a Sonnet
Under me bonnet
Dere's an Epic
In me ear,
Dere's a Novel
In me navel
Dere's a classic
Here somewhere.
Dere's a Movie
In me left knee
A long story
In me right,
Dere's a shorty

192

Inbetweeny
It is tickly
In de night.
Dere's a picture
In me ticker
Unmixed riddims
In me heart,
In me texture
Dere's a comma
In me fat chin
Dere is Art.
Dere's an Opera
In me bladder
A Ballad's
In me wrist
Dere is laughter
In me shoulder
In me guzzard's
A nice twist.
In me dreadlocks
Dere is syntax
A dance kicks
In me bum
Thru me blood tacks
Dere run true facts
I got limericks
From me Mum,
Documentaries
In me entries
Plays on history

In me folk,
Dere's a Trilogy
When I tink of three
On me toey
Dere's a joke.

*Benjamin Zephaniah*

# Watch Out, There's a Ghost About

*Watch out, there's a ghost about,*
Tall as the tallest tree,
*Watch out, there's a ghost about*
That can shrink to the size of a flea.

*Watch out, there's a ghost about*
Playing chase with the wind,
*Watch out, there's a ghost about*
And all it wants is a friend.

*Watch out, there's a ghost about*
Sliding under the door,
*Watch out, there's a ghost about,*
Drifting across the floor.

*Watch out, there's a ghost about*
Hovering behind your chair,
*Watch out, there's a ghost about*
Combing cold hands through your hair.

*Watch out, there's a ghost about*
And it's getting bolder,
*Watch out, there's a ghost about*
Sitting on your shoulder . . .

*Kevin McCann*

## Hard to Please

I don't like stings from wasps or bees
I don't like friends to see my knees
I don't like war, don't like disease
That's why they call me hard to please.

I don't like milk that smells like cheese
I don't like coughs that start to wheeze
I don't like spots you have to squeeze
That's why they call me hard to please.

I don't like baths that start to freeze
I don't like friends who taunt and tease
I don't like last week's mushy peas
That's why they call me hard to please.

*Steve Turner*

## Clap-Clap Clappity Clap

*This is a circular action/clapping song. Any names and actions can be included, to suit the group.*

*A*ngela, *Angela,* dance with me,
Over the water and over the sea.
   *Clap-clap, clappity clap.*

*Bridget, Bridget,* laugh with me,
Over the water and over the sea.
   *Clap-clap, clappity clap.*

*Caroline, Caroline,* sing with me,
Over the water and over the sea.
   *Clap-clap, clappity clap.*

*Deborah, Deborah,* talk with me,
Over the water and over the sea.
    *Clap-clap, clappity clap.*

*Erica, Erica,* write to me,
Over the water and over the sea.
    *Clap-clap, clappity clap.*

*Fiona, Fiona,* walk with me,
Over the water and over the sea.
    *Clap-clap, clappity clap.*

*Gerri, Gerri,* play with me,
Over the water and over the sea.
    *Clap-clap, clappity clap.*

*Hannah, Hannah,* read with me,
Over the water and over the sea.
    *Clap-clap, clappity clap.*

*Isobel, Isobel,* hop with me,
Over the water and over the sea.
    *Clap-clap, clappity clap.*

*Jackie, Jackie,* stroll with me,
Over the water and over the sea.
    *Clap-clap, clappity clap.*

(And so on, while there are enough names)

Children all, wherever you may be,
Over the water and over the sea.
> *Clap-clap, clappity clap.*

Come in a circle, clap with me,
Over the water and over the sea.
> *Clap-clap, clappity clap.*

*Jennifer Curry*

# from 'The Purple Llama Wishes You . . .'

The sky can be anything but green:
Aubergine  indigo  rose
chrome
mouse grey  elephant;
hues with a warmth on their lips
from the brown earth:
umber  amber
sienna  ochre;
and the blues:
azure  sapphire
lapis lazuli
feathery peacock  watery ultramarine
night navy

and I'll love you till
the sky is viridian  celadon  emerald  lime
flamingoes are purple
and their question marks
don't answer yes
and the alphabet stops at x

*Judith Green*

## *Where the Bee Sucks*

Where the bee sucks, there suck I:
In a cowslip's bell I lie;
There I couch when owls do cry.
On the bat's back I do fly
After summer merrily.
Merrily, merrily shall I live now
Under the blossom that hangs on the bough.

*William Shakespeare*

## *There Was an Old Lady*

There was an old lady who swallowed a fly.
I don't know why she swallowed a fly.
Perhaps she'll die.

The same old lady, she swallowed a spider
That wriggled and jiggled and tickled inside her.
She swallowed the spider to catch the fly.
I don't know why she swallowed a fly.
Perhaps she'll die.

The same old lady, she swallowed a bird.
How absurd to swallow a bird!
She swallowed the bird to catch the spider,
She swallowed the spider to catch the fly.
I don't know why she swallowed a fly.
Perhaps she'll die.

The same old lady, she swallowed a cat.
Fancy that! She swallowed a cat.
She swallowed the cat to catch the bird.
She swallowed the bird to catch the spider,
She swallowed the spider to catch the fly.
I don't know why she swallowed a fly.
Perhaps she'll die.

The same old lady, she swallowed a dog.
She went the whole hog when she swallowed the dog.
She swallowed the dog to catch the cat,
She swallowed the cat to catch the bird,
She swallowed the bird to catch the spider,
She swallowed the spider to catch the fly.
I don't know why she swallowed a fly.
Perhaps she'll die.

The same old lady, she swallowed a cow.
I don't know how she swallowed the cow.
She swallowed the cow to catch the dog,
She swallowed the dog to catch the cat,
She swallowed the cat to catch the bird,
She swallowed the bird to catch the spider,
She swallowed the spider to catch the fly.
I don't know why she swallowed a fly.
Perhaps she'll die.

The same old lady, she swallowed a horse.
She died, of course.

*Anon.*

## *Move It*

You can wiggle you can waggle
You can wobble you can hop
You can hover you can hobble
You can hang until you drop
You can swivel you can scramble
You can shimmy-shimmy hips
and you can slide, but don't slip
Slide, but don't slip

You can tumble you can totter
You can tickle you can leap
You can do the locomotion
You can linger you can creep
You can kick, yes you can-can
You can jive and you can skip
and you can slide, but don't slip
Slide, but don't slip

You can scribble you can stutter
You can really rock and roll
You can rave and you can ramble,
you can bat and you can bowl
You can bump and bossa nova
You can bounce and you can grip
and you can slide, but don't slip
Slide, but don't slip

*Chorus/bassline:* Slide, but don't slip. Slide, but don't slip.
*(or any combination of words from the poem)*

*Linda Lee Welch*

## *Playing Pooh-sticks with Trains*

We heard the faint oohooing in the distance –
our clue, and holding hands we skeltered to the iron bridge
that spanned the track to catch a glimpse
of passengers or driver, who might glance
and wave at us.

We stood on tiptoe, fingers pulling on the parapet,
chins rested on the rusty edge, waiting with anticipation
for the metal metal clatter dashing to a station
down the line and maybe far away as Kathmandu, and to
    get
someone to wave at us.

And here it comes!
We feel vibrations through our bones
and hunch our shoulders in the noisy pleasure,
waving at a blur of strangers,
then swapping sides so quickly
we try not to miss a carriage – it's like playing Pooh-sticks
with a train;
and just before it disappears on its iron river,
a lady waves!

*Judith Green*

## *Kubla Khan*

In Xanadu did Kubla Khan
A stately pleasure-dome decree:
Where Alph, the sacred river, ran
Through caverns measureless to man
  Down to a sunless sea.
So twice five miles of fertile ground
With walls and towers were girdled round:
And here were gardens bright with sinuous rills,
Where blossomed many an incense-bearing tree;
And here were forests ancient as the hills
Enfolding sunny spots of greenery.
But oh! that deep romantic chasm which slanted
Down the green hill athwart a cedarn cover!
A savage place! as holy and enchanted
As e'er beneath a waning moon was haunted
By woman wailing for her demon-lover!
And from this chasm, with ceaseless turmoil seething,
As if this earth in fast thick pants were breathing,
A mighty fountain momently was forced:
Amid whose swift half-intermitted burst
Huge fragments vaulted like rebounding hail,
Or chaffy grain beneath the thresher's flail;
And 'mid these dancing rocks at once and ever
It flung up momently the sacred river.

Five miles meandering with a mazy motion
Through wood and dale the sacred river ran,
Then reached the caverns measureless to man,
And sank in tumult to a lifeless ocean:
And 'mid this tumult Kubla heard from far
Ancestral voices prophesying war!
　　The shadow of the dome of pleasure
　　Floated midway on the waves;
　　Where was heard the mingled measure
　　From the fountain and the caves.
It was a miracle of rare device,
A sunny pleasure-dome with caves of ice!

　　A damsel with a dulcimer
　　In a vision once I saw:
　　It was an Abyssinian maid,
　　And on her dulcimer she played,
　　Singing of Mount Abora.
　　Could I revive within me
　　Her symphony and song,
　　To such a deep delight 'twould win me,
That with music loud and long,
I would build that dome in air,
That sunny dome! those caves of ice!
And all who heard should see them there,
And all should cry, Beware! Beware!
His flashing eyes, his floating hair!
Weave a circle round him thrice,
And close your eyes with holy dread,
For he on honey-dew hath fed,
And drunk the milk of Paradise.

*Samuel Taylor Coleridge*

## *A Green Cornfield*

The earth was green, the sky was blue:
  I saw and heard one sunny morn
A skylark hang between the two,
  A singing speck above the corn;

A stage below, in gay accord,
  White butterflies danced on the wing,
And still the singing skylark soared,
  And silent sank and soared to sing.

The cornfield stretched a tender green
  To right and left beside my walks;
I knew he had a nest unseen
  Somewhere among the million stalks.

And as I paused to hear his song
  While swift the sunny moments slid,
Perhaps his mate sat listening long,
  And listened longer than I did.

*Christina Rossetti*

# *Jabberwocky*

'Twas brillig, and the slithy toves
  Did gyre and gimble in the wabe:
All mimsy were the borogoves,
  And the mome raths outgrabe.

'Beware the Jabberwock, my son!
  The jaws that bite, the claws that catch!
Beware the Jubjub bird, and shun
  The frumious Bandersnatch!'

He took his vorpal sword in hand:
  Long time the manxome foe he sought –
So rested he by the Tumtum tree,
  And stood awhile in thought.

And, as in uffish thought he stood,
  The Jabberwock, with eyes of flame,
Came whiffling through the tulgy wood,
  And burbled as it came!

One, two! One, two! And through and through
  The vorpal blade went snicker-snack!
He left it dead, and with its head
  He went galumphing back.

'And hast thou slain the Jabberwock?
  Come to my arms, my beamish boy!
O frabjous day! Callooh! Callay!'
  He chortled in his joy.

'Twas brillig, and the slithy toves
  Did gyre and gimble in the wabe:
All mimsy were the borogoves,
  And the mome raths outgrabe.

*Lewis Carroll*

## *What Will I Be When I Grow Up?*

Mum says: 'Happy.'
Dad says: 'Older – and taller.'
My sister Kate says: 'Just as . . . nice!'
My mate Sam says: 'Still my best friend.'
Auntie Jessie says: 'Anything you want to be.'
Uncle Jack says: 'An adult!'
My teacher says: 'Wiser.'
And Gran says: 'Brilliant.'
And I say: How do they know?

*James Carter*

# June

## A Fairy Song

Over hill, over dale,
   Thorough bush, thorough brier,
Over park, over pale,
   Thorough flood, thorough fire!
I do wander everywhere,
   Swifter than the moon's sphere;
And I serve the fairy queen,
   To dew her orbs upon the green;
The cowslips tall her pensioners be;
   In their gold coats spots you see;
Those be rubies, fairy favours,
   In those freckles live their savours:
I must go seek some dewdrops here,
And hang a pearl in every cowslip's ear.

*William Shakespeare*

## Past and Present

I remember, I remember,
The house where I was born,
The little window where the sun
Came peeping in at morn;
He never came a wink too soon,
Nor brought too long a day,
But now, I often wish the night
Had borne my breath away!

I remember, I remember,
The roses, red and white,
The violets, and the lily-cups,
Those flowers made of light!
The lilacs where the robin built,
And where my brother set
The laburnum on his birthday, –
The tree is living yet!

I remember, I remember,
Where I was used to swing,
And thought the air must rush as fresh
To swallows on the wing;
My spirit flew in feathers then,
That is so heavy now,
And summer pools could hardly cool
The fever on my brow!

I remember, I remember,
The fir trees dark and high;
I used to think their slender tops
Were close against the sky:
It was a childish ignorance,
But now 'tis little joy
To know I'm farther off from heaven
Than when I was a boy.

*Thomas Hood*

# Night Lights

There is no need to light a night-light
On a light night like tonight;
For a night-light's light's a slight light
When the moonlight's white and bright.

*Anon.*

## *May the Road Rise to Meet You*

*This heartfelt Irish blessing by an unknown author is sometimes quoted as an expression of good wishes at times of parting.*

May the road rise to meet you,
May the wind be always at your back.
May the sun shine warm upon your face,
The rains fall soft upon your fields.

And until we meet again,
May God hold you in the palm of his hand.
May God be with you and bless you;
May you see your children's children.

May you be poor in misfortune,
Rich in blessings,
May you know nothing but happiness
From this day forward.

May the road rise to meet you,
May the wind be always at your back.
May the warm rays of sun fall upon your home
And may the hand of a friend always be near.

May green be the grass you walk on,
May blue be the skies above you,
May pure be the joys that surround you,
May true be the hearts that love you.

*Anon.*

## *Ladybird*

Ishy Bishy Barney Bee
Count your blessings . . . 1.2.3.
Count your blessings, count your spots,
Count your pretty polka dots.

Ishy Bishy Barney Bee
Count your spots, then off you flee!
Scarlet jewel, precious gem . . .
4.5.6.7.8.9.10.

Ishy Bishy Barney Bee
What does spider eat for tea?
Hurry home, for I have heard
She licks the spots off ladybirds!

*Celia Gentles*

Ishy Bishy Barney Bee: Norfolk dialect for ladybird

## The Fastest Kid in School

I am the fastest kid in school.
I have the quickest feet.
There's no one who can match my speed.
I simply can't be beat.
There's nothing you can do or say
to beat me in a race.
I'll always be victorious.
I'll always win first place.
I'll beat you running up a hill.
I'll beat you on the track.
I'll beat you walking on my hands
or bouncing on my back.
I'll win on any given day!
Just pick the time and place!
I know you think you beat me,
but I let you win the race!

*Darren Sardelli*

## Tick Tock

*Half audience repeat each line, other half chant 'tick-tock tick-tock.' Or can be done as a round.*

Clocks are ticking.
Cogs are clicking.
Pendulums swinging.
Bells are ringing.
Clocks are chiming.
The hours they're timing.
The hands move round
with a tick-tock sound.

Clocks go tick.
Cogs go click.
Pendulums swing.
Alarm bells ring.
Clocks chime
to tell the time.
Hands go round
with a tick-tock sound.

*Geraldine Aldridge*

## *What Is Pink?*

What is pink? A rose is pink
By the fountain's brink.
What is red? A poppy's red
In its barley bed.
What is blue? The sky is blue
Where the clouds float through.
What is white? A swan is white
Sailing in the light.
What is yellow? Pears are yellow
Rich and ripe and mellow.
What is green? The grass is green,
With small flowers between.
What is violet? Clouds are violet
In the summer twilight.
What is orange? Why, an orange,
Just an orange!

*Christina Rossetti*

## *Coolscorin' Matchwinnin' Celebratin' Striker!*

I'm a shirt removin' crowd salutin'
handstandin' happy landin'
rockin' rollin' divin' slidin'
posin' poutin' loud shoutin'
pistol packin' smoke blowin'
flag wavin' kiss throwin'
hipswingin' armwavin'
breakdancin' cool ravin'
shoulder shruggin' team huggin'
hot shootin' rootin' tootin'
somersaultin' fence vaultin'
last-minute goal grinnin'
shimmy shootin' shin spinnin'
celebratin' cup winnin' STRIKER!

*Paul Cookson*

## Caterpillar Salad Rap

Caterpillar salad, butterfly flan
ants from the pantry boiled in a pan
bumble crumble, waspy jam
beetle treacle, fleas with ham
leech quiche, maggots-in-a-clam
lice in your rice like grains of sand
worm spaghetti on your hand
ladybird curd, that's the plan –
caterpillar salad, butterfly flan

*Philip Burton*

## The Hamster's Revenge

No one realized, nobody knew
The hamster was sleeping inside dad's shoe.

He put in his foot and squashed flat its nose
So it opened its jaws and chomped on his toes.

While howling and yowling and hopping like mad
The hamster wreaked further revenge on my dad.

It scampered and scurried up his trouser leg
And this time bit something much softer instead.

His eyes bulged and popped like marbles on stalks
And watered while walking the strangest of walks.

His ears wiggled wildly while shooting out steam
All the dogs in the town heard his falsetto scream.

His face went deep purple, his hair stood on end,
His mouth like a letter box caught in the wind.

The hamster's revenge was almost complete . . .
Dad couldn't sit down for seventeen weeks.

Now dad doesn't give the hamster a chance . . .
He wears stainless-steel socks and hamster-proof pants.

*Paul Cookson*

## Make Friends with a Tree

Give a tree a squeeze,
give a tree a hug,
join in celebration
with every bird and bug,

with every bat and badger,
with beetles and with bees,
a new year's resolution,
show kindness to the trees.

Make friends with a tree,
make friends with a tree,
hug a tree, go on show it
you really care, let a tree know it.
Make friends with a tree,
make friends with a tree.

Trees are always homes
to every sort of creature.
In a flat and empty landscape
a tree is a special feature.

Trees can be deciduous,
pine trees are coniferous,
but trees will never hurt you
no tree is carnivorous!

So treat a tree politely,
show it you're sincere.
Long after we have disappeared
trees will still be here.

Make friends with a tree,
make friends with a tree,
hug a tree, go on show it
you really care, let a tree know it.
Make friends with a tree,
make friends with a tree.

Snuggle up to a sycamore,
cuddle up to a pine,
wrap your arms around an oak,
enjoy a joke with a lime.

A tree will always listen,
tell your troubles to a tree.
To the mystery of life
An ash may hold the key.

So don't be abrupt with a birch,
don't try to needle a pine.
Don't interrupt a horse chestnut,
don't give a tree a hard time.

Make friends with a tree,
make friends with a tree,
hug a tree, go on show it
you really care, let a tree know it.
Make friends with a tree,
make friends with a tree.

A tree is a living thing,
it's not just a lump of wood.
Trees in Sherwood Forest
know all about Robin Hood.

A tree can tell us stories,
a tree knows history,
so in this world of fake and sham
let's celebrate truth in a tree.

Make friends with a tree,
make friends with a tree,
hug a tree, go on show it
you really care, let a tree know it.
Make friends with a tree,
make friends with a tree.

*Brian Moses*

## *Above the Dock*

Above the quiet dock in midnight,
Tangled in the tall mast's corded height,
Hangs the moon. What seemed so far away
Is but a child's balloon, forgotten after play.

*T. E. Hulme*

## The Three-headed Dog
### *A Poem for Three Contrasting Voices*

Dog 1:     I'm Nip.
Dog 2:     I'm Ripper.
Dog 3:     My name is Guss.
All:     We are the monster called Cerberus!

Dog 1:    I'm feeling hungry.
Dog 2:    I like to howl.
Dog 3:    I've found the dinner bowl.
All:      Growl! Growl! Growl!

Dog 1:    I'm chewing gristle.
Dog 2:    I like to whine.
Dog 3:    I've grabbed the greasy bits.
All:      Mine! Mine! Mine!

Dog 1:    I'm sniffing tree trunks.
Dog 2:    I like a nap.
Dog 3:    I'm gnawing rabbit bones.
All:      Yap! Yap! Yap!

Dog 1:    I'm smelling danger.
Dog 2:    I like the dark.
Dog 3:    I'm hearing sneaky feet.
All:      Bark! Bark! Bark!

Dog 1:    I've caught a burglar.
Dog 2:    I like to fight.
Dog 3:    I've pinned him to the ground.
All:      Bite! Bite! Bite!

Dog 1:    We are the winners.
Dog 2:    We like to score.
Dog 3:    We're feeling sleepy now.
All:      Snore! Snore! Snore!

| | |
|---|---|
| Dog 1: | I'm Nip. |
| Dog 2: | I'm Ripper. |
| Dog 3: | My name is Guss. |
| All: | We are the monster called CER-BER-US!! |

*Clare Bevan*

## *The Dying Airman*

A handsome young airman lay dying,
And as on the aerodrome he lay,
To the mechanics who round him came sighing,
The last dying words did he say:
'Take the cylinders out of my kidneys,
The connecting-rod out of my brain,
Take the cam-shaft from out of my backbone,
And assemble the engine again.'

*Anon.*

## I've Never Seen
### (after John Rice)

*I've never seen* a fridge climb a tree.
*I've never seen* a dog as small as a bee.
*I've never seen* a lamp-post shake my hand.
*I've never seen* a tiger play in a band.

*I've never seen* a pigeon smoke a pipe.
*I've never seen* an elephant learn to type.
*I've never seen* a television dance a jig.
*I've never seen* a pillar-box swallow a pig.

*I've never seen* a feather that weighed a ton.
*I've never seen* an igloo built on the sun.
*I've never seen* a mountain wear a hat.
*I've never seen* a caterpillar catapult a cat.

Have you?

*Charles Thomson*

## *When a Knight Won His Spurs*

When a knight won his spurs, in the stories of old,
He was gentle and brave, he was gallant and bold;
With a shield on his arm and a lance in his hand
For God and for valour he rode through the land.

No charger have I, and no sword by my side,
Yet still to adventure and battle I ride,
Though back into storyland giants have fled,
And the knights are no more and the dragons are dead.

Let faith be my shield and let joy be my steed
'Gainst the dragons of anger, the ogres of greed;
And let me set free, with the sword of my youth,
From the castle of darkness the power of the truth.

*Jan Struther*

## *Christy's Rap*

There's a boy down at the pool who said he couldn't
    swim;
First he didn't want to go, then he wouldn't get *in* . . .
Now you won't believe it but that boy is so cool,
He's the meanest, keenest swimmer in the local swimming
    pool.
*With a dip, dart, glide and slide,*
*Slither, slather, splish!*

There's a boy down at the pool who wouldn't swim on his
    back;
First he wouldn't try, then one day he got the knack.
Now you won't believe it but that boy is like a fish,
He's the meanest, keenest swimmer who'll swim any stroke
    you wish.
*With a dip, dart, glide and slide,*
*Slither, slather, splish!*

There's a boy down at the pool who would never try the
    jumps,
Then one day he took a deep breath and quickly came up
    trumps.

Now you won't believe it but you cannot keep him out;
He's the meanest, keenest swimmer without *any* drop of
  doubt!
*With a dip, dart, glide and slide,*
*Slither, slather, splish;*
*With an under, over, curve and swerve . . .*

*That boy thinks he's a fish!*

Judith Nicholls

## Do It Yourself

When Father decides to mend things,
he gets his hammer and saw,
some nails and screws and pliers
and hinges for the door.

And the dog says woof,
  woof, woof;
And the cat says miaow,
  miaow, miaow;
And the pictures fall from the wall,
  crash.

When Dad tries to fix a cupboard
my dog hides in her bed,
my cat goes behind the curtains
with his paws up to his head.

And the dog says woof,
    woof, woof;
And the cat says miaow,
    miaow, miaow;
And the pictures fall from the wall,
    crash.

Our house is held together
with sticky tape and string,
and we're running out of bandages
to wrap poor Father in.

And the dog says woof,
    woof, woof;
And the cat says miaow,
    miaow, miaow;
And the pictures fall from the wall,
    crash.

*Robin Mellor*

## *Take a Poem*

Why not take a poem
Wherever you go?
pop it in your pocket
nobody will know

Or take it to your classroom
stick it on the wall
tell them all about it
read it in the hall

Take it to the bathroom
tuck it up in bed
take the time to learn it
keep it in your head

Take it for a day trip
take it on a train
fold it as a hat
when it starts to rain

Take it to a river
fold it as a boat
pop it in the water
hope that it will float

Take it to a hilltop
fold it as a plane
throw it up skywards
time and time again

Take it to a postbox
send it anywhere
out into the world
with
      tender
           loving
                care

*James Carter*

## It's Not the Same Any More

It's not the same since Patch died.
Sticks are just sticks.
Never thrown, never fetched.

It's not the same.
Tennis balls lie still and lifeless.
The urge to bounce them has gone.

It's not the same now.
I can't bring myself to whistle.
He won't hear me.

His collar hangs on the hook
And his name tag and lead are dusty.

His basket and bowl are in a plastic bag
Lying at an angle on the garage shelf.

My new slippers will never be chewed.

I can now watch the telly in peace, uninterrupted.
No mad barking and leaping at the best bits.

I don't have to share my sweets and biscuits
And then wipe the drool off my hands.

It's just not the same any more.
When Patch died a small part of me died too.

All that's left is a mound of earth
And my hand-made cross underneath the apple tree.

All that's left are the memories.
Thousands of them.

It's just not the same any more.

*Paul Cookson*

## The Things Mums Say . . .

Wake up!
Get up!
Out of bed!
Mind your feet!
Mind your head!
Don't run around.
Don't be late.
Look at your room!
What a state!
Put all your stuff away now, please.
Why can I never find my keys?
Close your mouth and eat your food.
Look at that!
Don't stare it's rude.
Elbows OFF the table please
Money doesn't grow on trees.
I won't tell you again . . .
Did you hear what I said?
I won't tell you again
It's time for bed.

*Michaela Morgan*

## *Infant Joy*

'I have no name:
'I am but two days old.'
What shall I call thee?
'I happy am,
'Joy is my name.'
Sweet joy befall thee!

Pretty joy!
Sweet joy but two days old,
Sweet joy I call thee:
Thou dost smile,
I sing the while,
Sweet joy befall thee!

*William Blake*

## Voices of Water

The water in the rain says

*Tick Tick Tack*

The water in the sleet says

*Slush*

The water in the ice says

*Crick Crick Crack*

The water in the snow says

*Hush*

The water in the sink says

*Slosh Slosh*

The water in the tap says

*Drip*

The water in the bath says

*Wash Wash*

The water in the cup says

*Sip*

The water in the pool says

*Splish Splash*

The water in the stream says

*Trill*

The water in the sea says

*Crish Crash*

The water in the pond . . .

stays still.

The water in the soil says

*Sow, Sow*

The water in the cloud says

*Give*

The water in the plant says

*Grow, Grow*

The water in the world says

*Live*

*Tony Mitton*

# Sound Test

The clock ticks slowly
**T-i-c-k T-o-c-k**
My heart pounds loudly
**Thump Thump Thump**
My restless hand drums fast
**Drum Drum Drum Drum**
I write as quickly as I can
**Scratch Scratch Scratch**
The silence is deafening
**SSSSSSSSSSSHHHHHHHH**
The clock strikes two
**Chime! Chime!**
The exam is over – I let out a loud sigh
**AHHHHHHHHHHHHH**

*Lisa Carter*

## *An Ace of Space*

You will not hear me make a sound.
I'm very shy and rarely found
For mostly I live underground.

You will not often see my face
But I can tell you I'm an ace
At engineering soil and space.

I build long tunnels, tall and wide,
With nose and claws that are my pride.
No walls of mine will fall inside.

> For I'm an ace
> Of soil and space,
> A brilliant engineer.

My coat is velvet, smooth and black.
I'm peaceful and avoid attack
Except on worms which are my snack.

The mounds I leave intend no ill;
They're evidence in fact of skill
And show I work with strength and will.

For I'm an ace
Of soil and space.
I don't intrude.
I'm never rude.
I do my job;
I'm not a yob.
Why can't they see
And leave me free?
For I'm an ace
Of soil and space –
A brilliant engineer!

*Jane Mann*

## *How to Get a Fox into a Matchbox*

You'll need one fox
And one matchbox.
Undress your fox,
Remove its smocks,
Its skirts or frocks,
Its shirts, its jocks,
Its shoes and socks.
Then trim its locks.

Then slim your fox.
First hide its chocs;
Then make your fox,
While timed by clocks,
Swim lakes and lochs
And lift large rocks
And fight an ox
And run round blocks.

Then fool your fox.
Claim – shock of shocks –
That your matchbox
Contains its chocs
And hens in flocks
Plus plump peacocks
And crates and crocks
Of foxfood stocks.

Unorthodox?
A paradox?
So what? A pox
On him who mocks
Or carps or knocks
Cos . . . Bless my socks!
There's now a fox
In my matchbox.

*Nick Toczek*

Unorthodox: *means not normal*
a paradox: *something that seems impossible or ridiculous*

## Celebrations
### *(Action Poem)*

Should I raise an arm like Shearer
or punch the air with glee
slap a high five with my team mates
hold finger to lips like Henry?

Should I run to the crowd and salute them
pull my shirt up over my head
strut with my own self-importance
or impress by being modest instead?

I'm dithering on this question
Perhaps I'll take a poll
to help me decide how to celebrate
if I ever score my first goal

*Susan Bates*

## One Old Ox

One old ox opening oysters,
Two toads totally tired
Trying to trot to Tewkesbury,
Three tame tigers taking tea,
Four fat friars fishing for frogs,
Five fairies finding fire-flies,
Six soldiers shooting snipe,
Seven salmon sailing in Solway,
Eight elegant engineers eating excellent eggs;
Nine nimble noblemen nibbling non-pareils,
Ten tall tinkers tasting tamarinds,
Eleven electors eating early endive,
Twelve tremendous tale-bearers telling truth.

*Anon.*

## The Song of Mr Toad

The world has held great Heroes,
  As history books have showed;
But never a name to go down to fame
  Compared with that of Toad!

The clever men at Oxford
  Know all that there is to be knowed,
But they none of them knew one half as much
  As intelligent Mr Toad!

The animals sat in the Ark and cried,
  Their tears in torrents flowed.
Who was it said, 'There's land ahead'?
  Encouraging Mr Toad!

The Army all saluted
  As they marched along the road.
Was it the King? Or Kitchener?
  No. It was Mr Toad!

The Queen and her Ladies-in-waiting
  Sat at the window and sewed.
She cried, 'Look! who's that *handsome* man?'
  They answered, 'Mr Toad.'

*Kenneth Grahame*

# July

## Farewell, Pete

I had a little dinosaur
Nothing would it eat
But a chocolate cupcake
And my best mate, Pete

At school it burst the football
It wasn't fond of sports
It gobbled up the goalposts
and Mr Walton's shorts

It chased my Auntie Emma
You should have heard her shout
But it didn't like my granny
In fact, it spat her out

*Roger Stevens*

## Omba Bolomba

Omba omba babalo pom,
Ambi pongalong, ding ding brom.
O pori, do pori slib slob slom,
Omba palomba babaloli dom.
   Pin pinni lili pot?
      Pin pinni plee!
   Bin binni pipi lot?
      Wa la pee!
Omba golomba babalo pom,
Ambika zambika zim zim zom!

*Gerard Benson*

## Lavender's Blue

Lavender's blue, dilly dilly: lavender's green;
When I am King, dilly dilly, you shall be Queen.
Who told you that, dilly dilly, who told you so?
'Twas my own heart, dilly dilly, that told me so.

Call up your men, dilly dilly, set them to work:
Some to the plough, dilly dilly, some to the cart;
Some to make hay, dilly dilly, some to thresh corn,
While you and I, dilly dilly, keep ourselves warm.

If I should die, dilly dilly, as well may hap,
Bury me deep, dilly dilly, under the tap;
Under the tap, dilly dilly, I'll tell you why,
That I may drink, dilly dilly, when I am dry.

*Anon.*

## I Hear America Singing

I hear America singing, the varied carols I hear,
Those of mechanics, each one singing his as it should be
    blithe and strong,
The carpenter singing his as he measures his plank or
    beam,
The mason singing his as he makes ready for work, or
    leaves off work,
The boatman singing what belongs to him in his boat,
    the deckhand singing on the steamboat deck,

249

The shoemaker singing as he sits on his bench, the hatter
 singing as he stands,
The wood-cutter's song, the ploughboy's on his way in
 the morning, or at noon intermission or at sundown,
The delicious singing of the mother, or of the young wife
 at work, or of the girl sewing or washing,
Each singing what belongs to him or her and to none else,
The day what belongs to the day – at night the party of
 young fellows, robust, friendly,
Singing with open mouths their strong melodious songs.

*Walt Whitman*

## The Dark Avenger
### for 2 voices

My dog is called The Dark Avenger.
*Hello, I'm Cuddles.*

She understands every word I say.
*Woof?*

Last night I took her for a walk.
*Woof! Walkies! Let's go!*

Cleverly, she kept three paces ahead.
*I dragged him along behind me.*

She paused at every danger, spying out the land.
*I stopped at every lamp-post.*

When the coast was clear, she sped on.
*I slipped my lead and ran away.*

Scenting danger, Avenger investigated.
*I found some fresh chip papers in the bushes.*

I followed, every sense alert.
*He blundered through the trees, shouting 'Oi, come 'ere!
Where are you?'*

Something – maybe a sixth sense – told me to stop.
*He tripped over me in the dark.*

There was a pale menacing figure ahead of us.
*Then I saw the white Scottie from next door.*

Avenger sprang into battle, eager to defend her master.
*Never could stand terriers!*

They fought like tigers.
*We scrapped like dogs.*

Until the enemy was defeated.
*Till Scottie's owner pulled him off – spoilsport!*

Avenger gave a victory salute.
*I rolled in the puddles.*

And came to check I was all right.
*I shook mud over him.*

'Stop it, you stupid dog!'
*He congratulated me.*

Sometimes, even The Dark Avenger can go too far.
*Woof!!*

*Trevor Millum*

## Shop Chat

My shop stocks:

          locks, chips,
          chopsticks,
          watch straps,
          traps, tops,
          taps, tricks,
          ship's clocks,
          lipstick and chimney pots.

What does your shop stock?

*Sharkskin socks.*

*Libby Houston*

## The Swan

Swan swam over the sea –
Swim, swan, swim;
Swan swam back again,
Well swum, swan.

*Anon.*

## Mela Menagerie

It was summertime,
the animals were having a mela.
  The elephants cooked
curried pumpkin with tikka masala,
  sun-shy frogs and mice
sheltered under the hood of a cobra,
  bears and cockatoos

swapped couplets in a mini *mushaira*,
    horses and camels
pranced and danced a fantastic bhangra,
    tigers took pot-shot
at juicy papayas for one paisa,
    lions showed off paws
decorated with delicate henna,
    donkeys for a laugh
crowned Mule their day-long Maharaja,
    pelicans swallowed
swords with mango chutney and paratha,
    Sindbad's ship sailed in
on waves of dolphin abracadabra,
    monkeys built bridges
recalling how they once helped Prince Rama,
    while Ali Baba
and forty rooks acted out life's drama.
    It was summertime,
the animals were having a mela.

*Debjani Chatterjee*

## *Shining Things*

I love all shining things –
    the lovely moon,
The silver stars at night,
    gold sun at noon.
A glowing rainbow in
    a stormy sky,
Or bright clouds hurrying
    when wind goes by.

I love the glow-worm's elf-light
    in the lane,
And leaves a-shine with glistening
    drops of rain,
The glinting wings of bees,
    and butterflies,
My purring pussy's green
    and shining eyes.

I love the street lamps shining
    through the gloom,
Tall candles lighted in
    a shadowy room,

New-tumbled chestnuts from
      the chestnut tree,
And gleaming fairy bubbles
      blown by me.

I love the shining buttons
      on my coat,
I love the bright beads round
      my mother's throat.
I love the coppery flames
      of red and gold,
That cheer and comfort me,
      when I'm a-cold.

The beauty of all shining things
      is yours and mine,
It was a *lovely* thought of God
      to make things shine.

*Elizabeth Gould*

## Lost

And how often have I told you
you won't find something
if you don't look for it

*I have looked*

and this room is a pit, an absolute shambles,
how do you expect to find anything in here
let alone your gym kit?

*That's not the problem. I need my gym things*
*but I know where everything is*

Are you serious? In these mountains of mess,
these dumps of dirty clothes?

*Yes. I drew a map. I thought*
*if I know where everything is*
*I won't have to tidy up. So I drew a map*
*of everything, even the cobwebs*

So if you know where everything is
what have you dragged me from my breakfast to find?

*The map.*

Dave Calder

## Muuuuuuummmmmmm

Can we have a kitten
Can we have a dog
Can we call her Frisky
Can we call him Bob?
I can take him out each day
I can brush his fur
I will buy the dog meat
and milk to make her purrr
Mum!!!

Oh . . . no . . .
Well –

Can we have a donkey
or can we have a horse
a monkey or a parrot
hamster or a snake?
Can we have a guinea pig
a peahen
or a stoat,
llama or a budgie
a rabbit or a goat?

Can we have a crocodile,
gibbon or an owl,
all the zoos are closing
there's lots and lots around . . .
A penguin would be really good
keep it in the bath
a hyena in the garden
          to make the milkman laugh.

No, WE DON'T WANT stick insects
and goldfish aren't much fun . . .

Oh, can we have a puppy . . .
          Mum
               Mum
                    Muuuuuuummmmmmmm.

*Peter Dixon*

## *Dumb Insolence*

I'm big for ten years old
Maybe that's why they get at me

Teachers, parents, cops
Always getting at me

When they get at me

I don't hit 'em
They can do you for that

I don't swear at 'em
They can do you for that

I stick my hands in my pockets
And stare at them

And while I stare at them
I think about sick

They call it dumb insolence

They don't like it
But they can't do you for it

*Adrian Mitchell*

## *Socks*

My local Gents' Outfitter stocks
The latest line in snazzy socks:
Black socks, white socks,
Morning, noon and night socks,
Grey socks, green socks,
Small, large and in between socks,
Blue socks, brown socks,
Always-falling-down socks,
Orange socks, red socks,
Baby socks and bed socks,
Purple socks, pink socks,
What-would-people-think socks,
Holey socks and frayed socks,
British Empire-made socks,
Long socks, short socks,
Any-sort-of-sport socks,
Thick socks, thin socks,
And 'these-have-just-come-in' socks.

Socks with stripes and socks with spots,
Socks with stars and polka dots,
Socks for ankles, socks for knees,
Socks with twelve-month guarantees,
Socks for aunties, socks for uncles,
Socks to cure you of carbuncles,
Socks for nephews, socks for nieces,
Socks that won't show up their creases,
Socks whose colour glows fluorescent,
Socks for child or adolescent,
Socks for ladies, socks for gents,
Socks for only fifty pence.

Socks for winter, socks for autumn,
Socks with garters to support 'em,
Socks for work and socks for leisure,
Socks hand-knitted, made-to-measure,
Socks of wool and polyester,
Socks from Lincoln, Leeds and Leicester,
Socks of cotton and elastic,
Socks of paper, socks of plastic,
Socks of silk-embroidered satin,
Socks with mottoes done in Latin,
Socks for soldiers in the army,
Socks to crochet or macramé,
Socks for destinations distant,
Shrink-proof, stretch-proof, heat-resistant.

Baggy socks, brief socks,
Union Jack motif socks,
Chequered socks, tartan socks,
School or kindergarten socks,
Sensible socks, silly socks,
Frivolous and frilly socks,
Impractical socks, impossible socks,
Drip-dry machine-only-washable socks,
Bulgarian socks, Brazilian socks,
There seem to be over a million socks!

With all these socks, there's just one catch –
It's hard to find a pair that match.

*Colin West*

## *Caterpillar*
### *(with hand actions)*

| | |
|---|---|
| Caterpillar, caterpillar,<br>Lots of feet. | (fingers crawl over surface:<br>desktop or knees) |
| Caterpillar, caterpillar,<br>Lots to eat. | (fingers and thumbs form<br>jaws and chew) |

Caterpillar, caterpillar,
Spin, spin, spin.

(fingers of each hand
intertwine, wriggling rapidly)

Caterpillar, chrysalis,
Change within.

(hands mesh with fingers
tucked inside, still wriggling)

Chrysalis, chrysalis,
Long, dark night.

(thumbs hook into each other,
fingers still wriggling)

Chrysalis, butterfly,
Take to flight.

(hands spread flat becoming
flapping wings, thumbs still
hooked together)

*Ian Larmont*

## *London Bridge Is Falling Down*

London Bridge is falling down,
  Falling down, falling down,
London Bridge is falling down,
  My fair lady.

Build it up with sticks and stones,
  Sticks and stones, sticks and stones,
Build it up with sticks and stones,
  My fair lady.

Sticks and stones will wear away,
  Wear away, wear away,
Sticks and stones will wear away,
  My fair lady.

Build it up with iron and steel,
  Iron and steel, iron and steel,
Build it up with iron and steel,
  My fair lady.

Iron and steel will rust away,
  Rust away, rust away,
Iron and steel will rust away,
  My fair lady.

Build it up with bricks and clay,
  Bricks and clay, bricks and clay,
Build it up with bricks and clay,
  My fair lady.

Bricks and clay will wash away,
  Wash away, wash away,
Bricks and clay will wash away,
  My fair lady.

Build it up with silver and gold,
  Silver and gold, silver and gold,
Build it up with silver and gold,
  My fair lady.

Silver and gold is stole away,
  Stole away, stole away,
Silver and gold is stole away,
  My fair lady.

Build it up with stone so strong,
  Stone so strong, stone so strong,
Then 'twill last for ages long,
  My fair lady.

*Anon.*

## Tiger

Through the grass the tiger stalks
another of his evening walks.
You never hear his silent stroll
as he pads near the waterhole.
It's not a place to stand and mope,
I'm glad I'm not an antelope.

*Stewart Henderson*

## Tornado

I'm a joyrider. I'm a twister.
Give up now. You can't resist.
Gun-slinger. Car slinger too.
 Watch out! I'll wake you and take you
and shake you about. Like a massive bonfire
in the distance. I will not tolerate
 resistance. Sharpshooter,

house looter, on the run.
Get in my way
and it won't be fun.
In my eye
it's as quiet
as a mouse.
Next minute
I'll destroy
your house.
Hide in the
cellar. Hide
in the bath.
I'll find you
if you're in
my path.
I'm a
tornado
bent on
trouble.
Behind me
is only
a pile
of rubble.

*Jill Townsend*

## When I Grow Up

I want to be:

A systems analyst,
A game-show panellist,
A pop star
With a guitar,
A technologist,
A psychologist,
A herpetologist,

A man who studies volcanoes
*An ecologist?*
No, a seismologist!

I want to be:

Something in the city,
Very pretty,
A fortune teller
A good speller,

A radar technician,
Always out fishin',
A clever magician,
A cosmetician,
A politician,

A dress designer,
A coal miner,
A good rhymer,
A charmer,
A pig farmer,

A rock and roller,
A South Pole explorer,
A moonwalker,
A New Yorker;

I want to be:

Stinking rich,
A wicked witch,
A private eye,
An engineer,
A life peer,

A DJ
OK?
A lead singer,
A right winger
For Liverpool,
Cool!

I want to be:

Taller,
Thinner,
A lottery winner!

But if none
Of these can be
I will remain
Yours truly
ME!

*Matt Simpson*

## *Full of Surprises*

This poem is full of surprises
Each line holds something new
This poem is full of surprises
Especially for you . . .

It's full of tigers roaring
It's full of loud guitars
It's full of comets soaring
It's full of shooting stars

It's full of pirates fighting
It's full of winning goals
It's full of alien sightings
It's full of rock and roll

It's full of rainbows beaming
It's full of eagles flying
It's full of dreamers dreaming
It's full of teardrops drying

It's full of magic spells
It's full of wizards' pointy hats
It's full of fairy elves
It's full of witches and black cats

It's full of dragons breathing fire
It's full of dinosaurs
It's full of mountains reaching higher
It's full of warm applause

It's full of everything you need
It's full of more besides
It's full of food, the world to feed
It's full of fairground rides

It's full of love and happiness
It's full of dreams come true
It's full of things that are the best
Especially for you

It's jammed and crammed and packed and stacked
With things both old and new
This poem is full of surprises
Especially for you.

*Paul Cookson*

## *To a Butterfly*

I've watched you now a full half-hour,
Self-poised upon that yellow flower;
And, little Butterfly! indeed
I know not if you sleep or feed.
How motionless! – not frozen seas
More motionless! And then
What joy awaits you, when the breeze
Hath found you out among the trees,
And calls you forth again!

This plot of orchard-ground is ours;
My trees they are, my Sister's flowers.
Here rest your wings when they are weary;
Here lodge as in a sanctuary!
Come often to us, fear no wrong;
Sit near us on the bough!
We'll talk of sunshine and of song,
And summer days, when we were young;
Sweet childish days, that were as long
As twenty days are now.

*William Wordsworth*

## *Hush Little Baby*

Hush little baby, don't say a word,
Papa's going to buy you a mocking bird.

And if that mocking bird won't sing,
Papa's going to buy you a diamond ring.

And if that diamond ring turns to brass,
Papa's going to buy you a looking glass.

And if that looking glass gets broke,
Papa's going to buy you a billy goat.

And if that billy goat should run away,
Papa's going to buy you another today.

*Anon.*

## *The Deadly Rattlesnake*

Thin as a rake
A rattlesnake
Beneath a rock
Beside a lake
Begins to wake
Before daybreak
And gives its tail
A noisy shake.

An empty ache
Informs the snake
That it now has
A move to make,
A fast to break
And no mistake.
It gives its tail
A second shake.

Now wide awake
The rattlesnake
Uncoils itself . . .
A thirst to slake,
A meal to take;

Time to forsake
Its lonely lair
With one last shake.

And real, not fake,
This hungry snake
With poisoned fangs
For killing's sake
Would turn down cake.
It wants raw steak.
And creatures' hearts
Are right to quake.

Beware the deadly rattlesnake!

*Nick Toczek*

# The Mouse, the Frog and the Little Red Hen

Once a Mouse, a Frog and a Little Red Hen,
Together kept a house;
The Frog was the laziest of frogs,
And lazier still was the Mouse.

The work all fell on the Little Red Hen,
Who had to get the wood,
And build the fires, and scrub, and cook,
And sometimes hunt the food.

One day, as she went scratching round,
She found a bag of rye;
Said she, 'Now who will make some bread?'
Said the lazy Mouse, 'Not I.'

'Nor I,' croaked the Frog as he drowsed in the shade,
Red Hen made no reply,
But flew around with bowl and spoon,
And mixed and stirred the rye.

'Who'll make the fire to bake the bread?'
Said the Mouse again, 'Not I,'
And, scarcely opening his sleepy eyes,
Frog made the same reply.

The Little Red Hen said never a word,
But a roaring fire she made;
And while the bread was baking brown,
'Who'll set the table?' she said.

'Not I,' said the sleepy Frog with a yawn;
'Nor I,' said the Mouse again.
So the table she set and the bread put on,
'Who'll eat this bread?' said the Hen.

'I will!' cried the Frog. 'And I!' squeaked the Mouse,
As they near the table drew:
'Oh, no, you won't!' said the Little Red Hen,
And away with the loaf she flew.

*Anon.*

## First Day of the Summer Holidays

Time to put the pens to bed
Time to put the books away
Time to hide the uniform
We're on Summer Holiday!

Time to switch my alarm clock off
Time to sleep and overlay
Time to lock the homework up
We're on Summer Holiday!

Time to zip my schoolbag up
And in the cupboard let it stay
With my boring shoes for school
We're on Summer Holiday!

Time for trainers, time for jeans
Time for riding on my bike
Time for football all day long
Time for doing what I like.

Time for camping out in tents
Time for having lots of fun
Time for swimming, time for grinning,
Eating ice creams in the sun.

Time for playing hide and seek
Time for climbing high up trees
Time to rope swing over ditches
Time for scratched and dirty knees.

Time for going out with mates
Time for playing any game
Time for watching videos
All day long if it should rain.

Time for tennis, time for cricket,
Time for friends to come and call
Time for doing everything
Or doing nothing much at all.

Time for laughter, time for jokes,
Time for fun and time to play
Time to fool so goodbye school!
We're on Summer Holiday!

*Paul Cookson*

## Seaside Song

It was a
sun-boiled, bright light, fried egg, hot skin, sun-tanned
sssizzzzzzler of a day.

It was a
pop song, ding-dong, candy floss, dodgem car, arcade, no
shade
smashing seaside town.

We had
a well time, a swell time, a real pell-mell time,
a fine time, a rhyme time, a super double-dime time.

We
beach swam, ate ham, gobbled up a chicken leg,
climbed trees, chased bees,
got stuck in sand up to our knees,
played chase, flew in space,
beat a seagull in a skating race,
rowed boats, quenched throats,
spent a load of £5 notes,
sang songs, hummed tunes,
played hide and seek in sandy dunes.

Did all these things
too much by far
that we fell asleep going back in the car
from the seaside.

*John Rice*

## *The Playground Monster*

It grabbed me
with its tarmac jaws
and then it tried
to bite me.

It grasped me
with its gravelly paws
and then it tried
to fight me.

I live in fear of walking
across its great black back.

I think it knows I'm talking.
It listens at a crack!

I fear its greedy darkness,
the way it seems to need

to reach out when I'm running
and grab me for a feed.

It grabbed me
with its tarmac jaws
and then it tried
to bite me.

It grasped me
with its gravelly paws
and then it tried
to fight me.

*Pie Corbett*

# Railway Stations
### (To be read quickly, until the last line)

Basildon, Basildon, Bangor and Beccles,
Erdington, Erdington, Elgin and Eccles,

Paddington, Paddington, Pembroke and Poole,
Gainsborough, Gainsborough, Glasgow and Goole,

Pontefract, Pontefract, Penzance and Porth,
Battersea, Battersea, Buxton and Borth,

Dunfermline, Dunfermline, Dundee and Diss,
Lancaster, Lancaster, Lincoln and Liss,

Harrogate, Harrogate, Harlech and Hayle,
Southampton, Southampton, Swansea and Swale,

Waterloo, Waterloo, Watford and Wem,
Dagenham, Dagenham, Dunblane and Drem,

Rochester, Rochester, Rochdale and Rye,
Windermere, Windermere, Wilmslow and Wye,

Crediton, Crediton, Clacton and Crewe,
I'd like to get off this train, wouldn't you?

*Tim Pointon*

## from *To Althea, from Prison*

Stone walls do not a prison make,
Nor iron bars a cage;
Minds innocent and quiet take
That for an hermitage:
If I have freedom in my love
And in my soul am free,
Angels alone, that soar above,
Enjoy such liberty.

*Richard Lovelace*

## *Daughter of the Sea*

bog seeper
moss creeper
growing restless  getting steeper

trickle husher
swish and rusher
stone leaper  splash and gusher

foam flicker
mirror slicker
pebble pusher  boulder kicker

still pool
don't be fooled
shadow tricker  keeping cool

leap lunger
crash plunger
free fall  with thunder under

garbage binner
dump it in her
never mind  her dog's dinner

plastic bagger
old lagger
oil skinner  wharf nagger

cargo porter
weary water
tide dragger  long lost daughter

of the sea
the sea the sea
has caught her up in its arms and set her free

*Philip Gross*

## *Dear Spider,*

Thanks for the invitation
to your cosy dinner for two.
I'd really love to come
but I can't think what to do.
I can't decide just what to wear
my clothes are all so fine
and I'm not certain where to find
a suitable sort of wine.
I'm not used to dining out,
it's really not my thing.
I tend to snatch my meals
when I am on the wing.
My mealtime conversation
is limited in kind.

In short I feel that
I really should decline.
It's not that I don't like you
but we are so far apart;
I can't see it working out
although you want my heart.

Yours sincerely
Fly

*Angela Topping*

## *Troll*

I'm a troll, foldy roll,
and I'm standing on my bridge.
I'm a troll, foldy roll,
and there's nothing in my fridge.
And I'm getting very hungry
for a nice sam-widge.
So I'll slap you on a slice
and I'll bite – SQUELCH! SQUIDGE!

Or I'll roll you and I'll fold you
in a big foldy roll.
Then I'll lick you and I'll stick you
in my great cake-hole.

I'm a troll, foldy roll,
and I aren't half strong.
And I'm big and I'm hairy
and I don't half pong.
And I gobble up people
though it's nasty and it's wrong.
Now it's time to give a roll
on my noisy dinner GONG!

*Tony Mitton*

# August

**1**

## *The Toilet Seat Has Teeth*

The bathroom has gone crazy
far beyond belief.
The sink is full of spiders
and the toilet seat has teeth!

The plughole in the bath
has a whirlpool underneath
that pulls you down feet first
and the toilet seat has teeth!

The toothpaste tube is purple
and makes your teeth fall out.
The toilet roll is nettles
and makes you scream and shout!

The towels have got bristles,
the bubble bath is glue,
the soap has turned to jelly
and it makes your skin bright blue.

The mirror's pulling faces
at everyone it can.
The shower's dripping marmalade
and blackcurrant jam.

The rubber ducks are breeding
and building their own nest
with shaving foam and tissues
in Grandad's stringy vest.

Shampoo is liquid dynamite,
there's petrol in the hairspray,
both will cure dandruff
when they blow your head away!

The bathroom has gone crazy
far beyond belief.
The sink is full of spiders
and the toilet seat has teeth!

The plughole in the bath
has a whirlpool underneath
that pulls you down feet first
and the toilet seat has teeth!

The toilet seat has teeth! Ow!
The toilet seat has teeth! Ow!
The toilet seat has teeth! Ow!
The toilet seat has teeth! Ow!

Crunch! Slurp! Munch! Burp!
The toilet seat has teeth! Ow!
Don't – sit – on – it!
The toilet seat has . . . ! Owwwww!

*Paul Cookson*

# Hurt No Living Thing

Hurt no living thing,
Ladybird nor butterfly,
Nor moth with dusty wing,
Nor cricket chirping cheerily,
Nor grasshopper, so light of leap,
Nor dancing gnat,
Nor beetle fat,
Nor harmless worms that creep.

*Christina Rossetti*

## *Shaun Short's Short Shorts*

Shaun Short bought some shorts.
The shorts were shorter than Shaun Short thought.
Shaun Short's short shorts were so short,
Shaun Short thought, *Shaun, you ought*
*Not to have bought shorts so short.*

*John Foster*

*4*

# Electric Guitars

I like electric guitars:
played mellow or moody
frantic or fast – on CDs
or tapes, at home or in
cars – live in the streets
at gigs or in bars.
I     like
electric
guitars:
played
choppy
l i k e
reggae
or angry
l i k e
rock or
chirpy
l i k e
jazz  or
strummy
l i k e
pop  or
h e a v y
l i k e
metal – it
bothers
me not.

I like electric guitars:

their strings and their straps

and their wild wammy bars – their

jangling and twanging and funky

wah-wahs – their fuzz boxes,

frets and multi-effects –

pick-ups, machine

heads, mahogany necks

– their plectrums, their wires

and big amplifiers. I like electric

guitars: played loudly, politely – dully

or brightly – daily or nightly – badly

or nicely. I like electric guitars:

bass, lead and rhythm –      I like electric guitars

I basically dig 'em –

*James Carter*

## from *Auguries of Innocence*

To see a World in a Grain of Sand
And a Heaven in a Wild Flower,
Hold Infinity in the palm of your hand
And Eternity in an hour.

*William Blake*

## *My Sari*

Saris hang on the washing line:
a rainbow in our neighbourhood.
This little orange one is mine,
it has a mango leaf design.
I wear it as a Rani would.
It wraps around me like sunshine,
it ripples silky down my spine,
and I stand tall and feel so good.

*Debjani Chatterjee*

## Roller Skaters

Flying by
on the winged-wheels
of their heels

Two teenage earthbirds
zig-zagging
down the street

Rising
unfeathered –
in sudden air-leap

Defying law
death and gravity
as they do a wheely

Landing back
in the smooth swoop
of youth

And faces gaping
gawking, impressed
and unimpressed

Only Mother watches – heartbeat in her mouth

*Grace Nichols*

# Old Mrs Lazibones

Old Mrs Lazibones
And her dirty daughter
Never used soap
And never used water.

> *Higgledy piggledy cowpat*
> *What d'you think of that?*

Daisies from their fingernails,
Birds' nests in their hair-O,
Dandelions from their ears –
What a dirty pair-O!

> *Higgledy piggledy cowpat*
> *What d'you think of that?*

Came a prince who sought a bride,
Riding past their doorstep,
'Quick,' said Mrs Lazibones,
'Girl, under the watertap.'

> *Higgledy piggledy cowpat*
> *What d'you think of that?*

Washed her up and washed her down,
Then she washed her sideways,
But the prince was far, far away,
He'd ridden off on the highways.

> *Higgledy piggledy cowpat*
> *What d'you think of that?*

*Gerda Mayer*

## Space Counting Rhyme

10 flying saucers, 10 flashing lights
9   glowing trails, 9 meteorites
8   sliver spaceships trying to find
7   lost aliens left behind
6   burning comets blazing fire
5   red rockets blasting higher
4   satellites, 4 radar dishes
3   stars shooting means 3 wishes
2   bright lights – the moon and sun
1   little me to shine upon

*Paul Cookson*

## *Body Poem*

The human body's a machine,
the spaceship of the self,
and perfect working order means
you're in the best of health.
The brain is the computer,
the mind, a kind of screen,
the human body's a machine
that comes in many colours,
but not green.

Or anything stripy.

*John Hegley*

**11**

## Gran Can You Rap?

Gran was in her chair she was taking a nap
When I tapped her on the shoulder to see if she could rap.
Gran can you rap? Can you rap? Can you Gran?
And she opened one eye and she said to me, Man,
   I'm the best rapping Gran this world's ever seen
   I'm a tip-top, slip-slap, rap-rap queen.

And she rose from her chair in the corner of the room
And she started to rap with a bim-bam-boom,
And she rolled up her eyes and she rolled round her head
And as she rolled by this is what she said,
   I'm the best rapping Gran this world's ever seen
   I'm a nip-nap, yip-yap, rap-rap queen.

Then she rapped past my dad and she rapped past my
   mother,
She rapped past me and my little baby brother.
She rapped her arms narrow she rapped her arms wide,
She rapped through the door and she rapped outside.
   She's the best rapping Gran this world's ever seen
   She's a drip-drop, trip-trap, rap-rap queen.

She rapped down the garden she rapped down the street,
The neighbours all cheered and they tapped their feet.
She rapped through the traffic lights as they turned red
As she rapped round the corner this is what she said,
　　　I'm the best rapping Gran this world's ever seen
　　　I'm a flip-flop, hip-hop, rap-rap queen.

She rapped down the lane she rapped up the hill,
And as she disappeared she was rapping still.
I could hear Gran's voice saying, Listen Man,
Listen to the rapping of the rap-rap Gran.
　　　I'm the best rapping Gran this world's ever seen
　　　I'm a –
　　　　　tip-top, slip-slap,
　　　　　　　nip-nap, yip-yap,
　　　　　　　　　hip-hop, trip-trap,
　　　　　　　　　　　touch yer cap,
　　　　　　　　　　　take a nap,
　　　　　　　　　　　　　happy, happy, happy, happy,
　　　　　　　　　　　　　rap – rap – queen.

*Jack Ousbey*

## *Going to the Olympics*
### *(for several individuals and some small groups)*

1      I can cycle.

2      I can run.

3      I can outswim anyone.

4      I can high jump.
         Watch me fly.
         No one else can jump as high.

ALL    Off to the Olympic Games.
         Watch our team. Hear their names.

5      I'm a sprinter –
         feet a blur.

6      The Marathon's what I prefer.

7      We like team sports –
         volleyball,
         football, hockey – love them all.

ALL    Off to the Olympic Games.
         Watch our team. Hear their names.

8     I'm a table tennis whizz.
Watch me dart.
Watch me fizz.

9     The decathlon's
what I do –
pretty tough, but I'll come through.

ALL     Off to the Olympic Games.
Watch our team. Hear their names.

10     We are rowers –
stretch – heave.
Hard to follow Matt and Steve!

11     I do shot put:
balance, spin,
throw – and keep my big feet in!

ALL     Off to the Olympic Games.
Watch our team. Hear their names.

12     I can throw the javelin.
Watch me.
I'm sure I can win.

7      We're spectators.
       We love sport.
       Every team needs our support.

ALL    Off to the Olympic Games.
       Watch our team. Hear their names.

*Jill Townsend*

## A Plate of Potatoes

A plate of potatoes, a plate of potatoes,
There's nothing as great
As a plate of potatoes!

Baked in foil, fried in oil,
There's nothing as great
As a plate of potatoes!

Cooked in a curry, boiled in a hurry,
There's nothing as great
As a plate of potatoes!

Stewed in a pot? Give me the lot!
There's nothing as great
As a plate of potatoes!

Mashed with cheese? Mmm, yes please!
There's nothing as great
As a plate of potatoes!

A plate of potatoes, a plate of potatoes,
There's nothing as great
As a plate of potatoes!

*Kaye Umansky*

## Are We There Yet?

Our car is full up to the brim,
our camping gear is all squashed in.
Robert's strapped in his car seat,
stuff is stashed around my feet.
Dad says, 'OK! We're all set!'
And Robert says,
        'Are we there yet?'

We haven't gone so very far
when Mum says, 'Oh no! Stop the car!
Turn round now! Go straight back home!
I've left the money by the phone.'
Dad says, 'How could you forget?'
And Robert says,
      'Are we there yet?'

We're crawling down the motorway,
there's heavy traffic in our way,
Mum is pulling out her hair,
We're not getting anywhere.
Dad says, 'There's no need to fret.'
And Robert says,
      'Are we there yet?'

Now Mum's stressed out and Dad is cross.
Mum won't admit she's got us lost.
'It shows a short cut down this lane.
This map is wrong! I'm not to blame!'
Dad says, 'I wish we'd never met!'
And Robert says,
      'Are we there yet?'

At last the camping ground's in sight.
It's raining. It's the dead of night.
'The gates are locked!' Mum starts to weep.
Robert yells. Dad goes to sleep.
Next day, the tent's up, soaking wet
and Robert says,
      'Are we there yet?

*Jane Clarke*

# Moonlight, Summer Moonlight

'Tis moonlight, summer moonlight,
All soft and still and fair;
The silent time of midnight
Shines sweetly everywhere,

But most where trees are sending
Their breezy boughs on high,
Or stooping low are lending
A shelter from the sky.

*Emily Brontë*

## Me and You

Tell me why you're crying,
Tell me why you're sad,
Tell me why you're silent,
Tell me what's so bad.

*I've got no one to talk to,*
*I'm always on my own,*
*I've got no one to call a friend,*
*I'm scared and all alone.*

Talk to me, I'll listen,
I'm sometimes lonely too,
Together we can beat it,
Together – me and you.

*Clive Webster*

## *My Dog*

My dog belongs to no known breed,
    A bit of this and that.
His head looks like a small haystack;
    He's lazy, smelly, fat.

If I say, 'Sit!' he walks away.
    When I throw stick or ball
He flops down in the grass as if
    He had no legs at all.

Then looks at me with eyes that say,
    'You threw the thing, not me.
You want it back? Then get it back.
    Fair's fair, you must agree.'

He is a thief. Last week but one
    He stole the Sunday roast
And showed no guilt at all as we
    Sat down to beans on toast.

The only time I saw him run –
    And he went like a flash –
Was when a mugger in the park
    Tried to steal my cash.

My loyal brave companion flew
  Like a missile to the gate
And didn't stop till safely home.
  He left me to my fate.

And would I swap him for a dog
  Obedient, clean and good,
An honest, faithful, lively chap?
  Oh boy, I would, I would!

*Vernon Scannell*

## The Conversation

*This is a poem for three voices, that of bird, worm and a narrator who says the first line of each stanza. The audience joins in by repeating the last two lines. The poet suggests possible use of costume, mime and musical accompaniment.*

Said the worm to the bird:
Is it cold up there
In the huge, great, shivery
Spacious air?

I've heard that the wind
When it blows, can blow
Somewhere to nowhere . . .
Is it so?
*Somewhere to nowhere . . .*
*Is it so?*

Said the bird to the worm:
I suppose you stay
in a tunnel of darkness
Night and day,
Squiggling, wriggling,
Smooth and pink.
It must be monotonous,
I should think?
*It must be monotonous,*
*I should think?*

Said the worm to the bird:
Is it nice to fly
From sky to tree
And from tree to sky?
Are the sun and the moon
And the stars as near
As the stones and the seed
To me, down here?
*As the stones and the seed*
*To me, down here?*

Said the bird to the worm:
What a tail you've got!
Do you find it gets
In the way a lot?
And wouldn't it be
A peculiar thing
If birds should squiggle
And worms could sing!
*If birds should squiggle*
*And worms could sing!*

Jean Kenward

## The Commentator

Good afternoon and welcome
To this international
Between England and Holland
Which is being played here today
At 4, Florence Terrace.
And the pitch looks in superb condition
As Danny Markey, the England captain,
Puts England on the attack.

Straight away it's Markey
With a lovely little pass to Keegan,
Keegan back to Markey,
Markey in possession here
Jinking skilfully past the dustbins;
And a neat flick inside the cat there
What a brilliant player this Markey is
And he's still only nine years old!
Markey to Francis,
Francis back to Markey,
Markey is through, he's through,
No, he's been tackled by the drainpipe:
But he's won the ball back brilliantly
And he's advancing on the Dutch keeper,
It must be a goal.
The keeper's off his line
But Markey chips him superbly
And it's a goal
No!
It's gone into Mrs Spence's next door.
And Markey's going round to ask for his ball back,
It could be the end of this international.
Now the door's opening
And yes, it's Mrs Spence,
Mrs Spence has come to the door
Wait a minute
She's shaking her head, she's shaking her head
She's not going to let England have their ball back
What is the referee going to do?
Markey's coming back looking very dejected

And he seems to be waiting . . .
He's going back,
Markey is going back for the ball!
What a brilliant and exciting move!
He waited until the front door was closed
And then went back for that ball.
And wait a minute,
He's found it, Markey has found that ball,
He has found the ball
And it's wonderful news
For the hundred thousand fans gathered here
Who are showing their appreciation
In no uncertain fashion.
But wait a minute,
The door is opening once more.
It's her, it's Mrs Spence
And she's waving her fist
And shouting something I can't quite understand
But I don't think it's encouragement.
And Markey's off,
He's jinked past her on the outside
Dodging this way and that
With Mrs Spence in hot pursuit
And he's past her, he's through,
What skills this boy has!
But Mr Spence is there too,
Mr Spence in the sweeper role
With Rover their dog.
Markey's going to have to pull out all the stops now.
He's running straight at him,

And now he's down, he's down on all fours'
What is he doing?
And Oh my goodness that was brilliant.
That was absolutely brilliant,
He's dived through Spence's legs;
But he's got him,
This rugged stopper has him by the coat
And Rover's barking in there too;
He'll never get out of this one.
But this is unbelievable!
He's got away
He has got away:
He wriggled out of his coat
And left part of his trousers with Rover.
This boy is real dynamite.
He's over the wall
He's clear
They'll never catch him now.
He's down the yard and on his way
And I don't think we're going to see
Any more of Markey
Until it's safe to come home.

*Gareth Owen*

## *Overheard on a Saltmarsh*

Nymph, nymph, what are your beads?

Green glass, goblin. Why do you stare at them?

Give them me.

        No.

Give them me. Give them me.

                No.

Then I will howl all night in the reeds,
Lie in the mud and howl for them.

Goblin, why do you love them so?

They are better than stars or water,
Better than voices of winds that sing,
Better than any man's fair daughter,
Your green glass beads on a silver ring.

Hush, I stole them out of the moon.

Give me your beads. I want them.

                                            No.

I will howl in a deep lagoon
For your green glass beads, I love them so.
Give them me. Give them.

                              No.

                                    *Harold Monro*

## *The Soldier*

If I should die, think only this of me:
That there's some corner of a foreign field
That is for ever England. There shall be
In that rich earth a richer dust concealed;
A dust whom England bore, shaped, made aware,
Gave, once, her flowers to love, her ways to roam,
A body of England's, breathing English air,
Washed by the rivers, blest by suns of home.

And think, this heart, all evil shed away,
A pulse in the eternal mind, no less
Gives somewhere back the thoughts by England given;
Her sights and sounds; dreams happy as her day;
And laughter, learnt of friends; and gentleness,
In hearts at peace, under an English heaven.

*Rupert Brooke*

## Overheard on Safari

Look!
There's a flock of elephants
Galumphing across the horizon.

*Herd of elephants.*

Of course I've heard of elephants.
I was just telling you,
I saw a flock of them over there.

### Herd!

Not from here you can't.
Unless you've got sharper ears than mine.
You can't hear them from here.
Even a big flock like that.

### It's a HERD of elephants.

Yes, I know. Of course it is.
I've got eyes in my head.
I was just pointing them out to you.

*Gerard Benson*

## The Footballer's Prayer

Our team
Which art eleven
Hallowed be thy game
Our match be won
Their score be none
On turf as we score at least seven
Give us today no daily red . . . card
And forgive us our lost passes
As we forgive those who lose passes against us
Lead us not into retaliation
And deliver us from all fouls
For three is the kick off
The power and scorer
For ever and ever
Full time

*Paul Cookson*

## Who's Baddest?

*Wolf One*:
Hello, fans. I'm the Big Bad Wolf
Of Little Piggies fame.
What's that? You want my autograph?
Most certainly. Your name?

*Wolf Two*:
Excuse *me*. *I'm* the Big Bad Wolf
Who tricked Red Riding Hood.
This wolf is an impostor!
My friends, this wolf is *good*.

*Wolf One*:
How dare you. *I'm* the Big Bad Wolf
No matter what you say.
Be off, before I huff and puff
And blow you clean away.

*Wolf Two*:
Aha! And so it's come to blows!
This wolf is really sad.
I'll go and eat his granny up
And *then* we'll see who's bad.

322

Huff, puff . . .
Gobble, gobble . . .
Huff, puff . . .
Gobble, gobble . . .
Huff, puff . . .
Gobble, gobble . . .

*Both*:
*Then* we'll see who's bad!

*Kaye Umansky*

# Christine Crump

First voice: Christine Crump is crunching crisps.
Second voice: Cheese and onion, cheese and onion.
First voice: Christine Crump has crunched them.

First voice: Christine Crump is crunching crisps.
Third voice: Smoky bacon, smoky bacon,
Second voice: Cheese and onion, cheese and onion.
First voice: Christine Crump has crunched them.

First voice: Christine Crump is crunching crisps.
Fourth voice: Ready salted, ready salted,
Third voice: Smoky bacon, smoky bacon,
Second voice: Cheese and onion, cheese and onion.
First voice: Christine Crump has crunched them.

First voice: Christine Crump is crunching crisps.
Fifth voice: Curry flavour, curry flavour,
Fourth voice: Ready salted, ready salted,
Third voice: Smoky bacon, smoky bacon,
Second voice: Cheese and onion, cheese and onion.
First voice: Christine Crump has crunched them.

First voice: Christine Crump is crunching crisps.
Sixth voice: Salt and vinegar, salt and vinegar,
Fifth voice: Curry flavour, curry flavour,
Fourth voice: Ready salted, ready salted,
Third voice: Smoky bacon, smoky bacon,
Second voice: Cheese and onion, cheese and onion.
First voice: Christine Crump has crunched them.

First voice: Christine Crump is feeling sick . . .
All together: Poor old Christine, poor old Christine,
First voice: She has indigestion.

*Colin West*

324

# Leisure Centre, Pleasure Centre

Through plate glass doors
    with giant red handles,
into light that's as bright
    as a million candles,
chlorine smells, the whole place steaming
    kids are yelling, kids are screaming.

Watch them
            *wave jump*
            *dive thump*
            *cartwheel*
            *free wheel*
            *look cute*
            *slip chute*
            *toe stub*
            *nose rub*
in the leisure centre, pleasure centre.

Sporty people laugh and giggle
    folk in swimsuits give a wiggle,
kids in the cafe are busy thinkin'
    if they can afford some fizzy drinkin'.
In the changing rooms the wet folk shiver,
    it's hard to get dressed as you shake and quiver.

And we go
>> *breast stroke*
>> *back stroke*
>> *two-stroke*
>> *big folk*
>> *hair soak*
>> *little folk*
>> *eye poke*
>> *no joke*

in the leisure centre, pleasure centre.

And now we're driving back home,
> fish 'n' chips in the car,
eyes are slowly closing
> but it's not very far.
Snuggle-wuggle up in fresh clean sheets
> a leisure centre trip is the best of treats!

Because you can
>> *keep fit*
>> *leap sit*
>> *eat crisps*
>> *do twists*
>> *belly flop*
>> *pit stop*
>> *fill up*
>> *with 7-Up*
>> *get going*
>> *blood flowing*
>> *look snappy*
>> *be happy*

in the leisure centre, pleasure centre.

*John Rice*

## Fish and Chips on Friday

They're eating pasta in Nebraska,
Tortillas in Dundee,
*But it's Friday,*
*So at our house*
*It's fish and chips for tea.*

Ratatouille in St Louis,
Faggots in Bahrain,
*But it's Friday,*
*So at our house*
*It's fish and chips again.*

Risotto in Somoto,
Crêpes Suzette in Mors,
*But it's Friday,*
*So at our house*
*It's fish and chips – of course.*

*John Coldwell*

## *Carnival*

Everybody love Carnival
Everybody love Carnival

Dress up in de costume
           Carnival
Dancin in de streets man
           Carnival

Feel the calypso beat
           Carnival
Lift up yo dancin feet
           Carnival

Everybody love Carnival
Everybody love Carnival

All over these islands
           Carnival

Even in Englan
           Carnival

Hug up to yo loved one
                    Carnival
Find yo a loved one
                    Carnival

Everybody love Carnival
Everybody love Carnival

*Angela Topping*

# When It's All Over

It's not for the smell of stale embrocation,
It's not for the days of anticipation,
It's not for the fist-waving glad celebration;

It's not for the fear that churns up your gut,
It's not for the pair of odd socks for good luck,
It's not for the changing room door banging shut;

It's not for the glint and the gleam of the studs,
It's not for the echo of the ball's ringing thud,
It's not for the feel of the soft clinging mud;

It's not for the frost on the pitch in the morning,
It's not for the substitutes standing round yawning,
It's not for the whistle that blasts without warning;

It's not for the mist that swirls round the posts,
It's not for the other team shrouded like ghosts,
It's not for the spectators lost in their coats;

It's not for the sweat on your head when you're running,
It's not for the threat of legs bruised, grey and numbing,
It's not for the net that deceives you with cunning:

But when it's all over,
When it's all done,
Whether we've lost,
But best if we've won –
We break out the soap,
High spirits and towels,
And sing in the showers
For hours and hours.

*Dave Ward*

# I'm Proud to Be

*I'm proud to be what I am*
*I'm proud to be what I am*

Could be English
Or from the Caribbean
 Could be Asian
 Or an African
 Could be fat or thin
 Or very small
 Four feet two
Or six feet tall

*I'm proud to be what I am*
*I'm proud to be what I am*

Could be black or white
Or yellow or brown
 Living in the poorer
 Side of town
 Might be slick
 Might be cool
Might not break laws
Might not break rules

*I'm proud to be what I am*
*I'm proud to be what I am*

May not have
  Designer gear
  May not have
  Great things to wear
  May not have
  A new CD
  May not have
    Your own TV.

*I'm proud to be what I am*
*I'm proud to be what I am*

It ain't what yer got
  It's who yer are
  Will take yer places
  'N' take yer far
Respect yer uncle, yer auntie
  Yer sister yer brother
  Yer cousin, yer niece
  Yer father yer mother

*I'm proud to be what I am*
*I'm proud to be what I am*

We're all the world's people
One family
   And that includes you
   And that includes me
   You are what you are
   You should be proud
So stand up straight
   And shout out loud

*I'm proud to be what I am*
*I'm proud to be what I am*

*Martin Glynn*

## Superman's Dog

Superman's dog – he's the best
Helping pets in distress
Red and gold pants and vest
'SD' on his chest.

Superman's dog – X-ray sight
Green bones filled with Kryptonite
Bright blue Lycra tights in flight
Faster than a meteorite

Better than Batman's robin
Rougher than Robin's bat
Faster than Spiderman's spider
Cooler than Catwoman's cat

Superman's dog – bionic scent
Crime prevention – his intent
Woof and tough – cement he'll dent
What's his name – Bark Kent!

*Paul Cookson*

# September

## The Owl

When cats run home and light is come,
  And dew is cold upon the ground,
And the far-off stream is dumb,
  And the whirring sail goes round,
  And the whirring sail goes round;
    Alone and warming his five wits,
    The white owl in the belfry sits.

When merry milkmaids click the latch,
  And rarely smells the new-mown hay,
And the cock hath sung beneath the thatch
  Twice or thrice his roundelay,
  Twice or thrice his roundelay;
    Alone and warming his five wits,
    The white owl in the belfry sits.

*Alfred, Lord Tennyson*

**2**

## *Thirty Days Hath September*

Thirty days hath September,
April, June, and November.
All the rest have thirty-one,
Except February alone,
Which has four and twenty-four
Till leap-year gives it one day more.

*Anon.*

**3**

## *Mrs Terminator*

Mrs Terminator – patrols the corridor
Mrs Terminator – paces up and down the floor
Mrs Terminator – her nostrils flare and steam
Breathing fire her face turns red when she begins to scream

*Exterminate! Exterminate! Zap! Pow! Wheeee!*
*Exterminate! Exterminate! Zap! Pow! Wheeee!*

Mrs Terminator – points and waves her hands
Mrs Terminator – bellows out her strict commands
Mrs Terminator – the veins upon her skull
Bulge and bubble just like pipes about to burst when full

*Exterminate! Exterminate! Zap! Pow! Wheeeee!*
*Exterminate! Exterminate! Zap! Pow! Wheeeee!*

Mrs Terminator – twenty-seven stone
Mrs Terminator – plays rugby on her own
Mrs Terminator – knuckles on the floor
Muscles just like Popeye's and whiskers on her jaw

*Exterminate! Exterminate! Zap! Pow! Wheeee!*
*Exterminate! Exterminate! Zap! Pow! Wheeee!*

Mrs Terminator – her favourite word is *SILENCE!*
Mrs Terminator – her favourite hobby's violence
Mrs Terminator – her school needs no bell
When she coughs the whole place stops and staff are
   scared as well

*Exterminate! Exterminate! Zap! Pow! Wheeee!*
*Exterminate! Exterminate! Zap! Pow! Wheeee!*

She's a Dalek dinnerlady, drives the kids and teachers crazy
Mrs Terminator is the boss . . . RIGHT!
She'll be back to see you later, she is Mrs Terminator
Mrs Terminator is the big big big BIG BOSS!

*Exterminate! Exterminate! Zap! Pow! Wheeee!*
*Exterminate! Exterminate! Zap! Pow! Wheeee!*

*Paul Cookson*

## At Dis Skool

Firs' day bak at skool . . . don't feel cool . . . bullies
   rule . . .
Heart pumpin' . . . racin' . . . jumpin' . . . thumpin'
Frightenin' . . . like lightenin' . . . bouncin' . . . from
One spot to annuva . . . ain't gotta sista or a bruvva
At dis skool . . .

Feel da feer growin' . . . hope I'm not showin' . . . feer
Breathin' hard . . . I'm blowin' . . . I'm nervus . . .
I'm worried . . . coz I'm alone . . . on my own . . .
Ain't feelin' cool . . . in da playground . . . bad kids rule
At dis skool . . .

Pepul kickin' ball . . . playin' marbles . . . conkers . . .
 jostlin'
Fightin' . . . actin' bonkers . . . da gazin' eyez . . . I
 realize . . .
I want dis moment ter end . . . don't want ter spend
Any more time . . . frettin' . . . I'm gettin' anxious . . . I
 really
Want dis moment . . . ter end . . . where is he . . . where is
he
There he is . . . my best friend . . . at dis skool

I ain't no trend setter . . . I ain't no blinger . . . I ain't got
A Gameboy . . . 'n' I ain't no good singa . . . not bad at
Computers . . . not too bad at gym . . . don't have slick
Trainers . . . know how ter swim . . . but one ting I
 have . . .
It ain't no lates' trend . . . I've got sumting more . . .
I have bes' friend . . . at dis skool . . .

*Martin Glynn*

## *Lady Lollipop*

Lollipop Lady
Lady Lollipop
She's got the power
To make the traffic stop

When she steps out
With her lollipop sign
The people on the pavement
Sure feel fine

They know they can go
They'll be OK
'Thank you very much'
Is what they all should say

To the Lollipop Lady
Lady Lollipop
She's got the power
To make the traffic stop

She's there for me
She's there for you
Standing in the rain
Doing what she's got to do

She makes it safe
For us to cross
Halts all the traffic
Shows who's boss

It's the Lollipop Lady
Lady Lollipop
She's got the power
To make the traffic stop

She's the Lollipop Lady
Lady Lollipop
And she's got the power
She's got the power
She's got the power
To make the traffic . . . STOP!

*Bernard Young*

# from *To Autumn*

Season of mists and mellow fruitfulness!
Close bosom-friend of the maturing sun;
Conspiring with him how to load and bless
With fruit the vines that round the thatch-eaves run;
To bend with apples the mossed cottage-trees,
And fill all fruit with ripeness to the core;
To swell the gourd, and plump the hazel shells
With a sweet kernel; to set budding more,
And still more, later flowers for the bees,
Until they think warm days will never cease,
For Summer has o'er-brimmed their clammy cells.

*John Keats*

## *Dick's Dog*

Dick had a dog
The dog dug
The dog dug deep
How deep did Dick's dog dig?

Dick had a duck
The duck dived
The duck dived deep
How deep did Dick's duck dive?

Dick's duck dived as deep as Dick's dog dug.

*Trevor Millum*

## *Rhubarb Crumble*

My mum calls rhubarb crumble
silver spangle
and she tells us
posh hotels serve nothing else.

*Good!* my brother says.
He eats for England
and couldn't care less

but I bet the posh hotels
wouldn't sell it
if they used as little sugar
as my mum does,
silver spangle or not.

*Judith Green*

**9**

## *The Walrus and the Carpenter*

The sun was shining on the sea,
  Shining with all his might:
He did his very best to make
  The billows smooth and bright –
And this was odd, because it was
  The middle of the night.

The moon was shining sulkily,
  Because she thought the sun
Had got no business to be there
  After the day was done –
'Its very rude of him,' she said,
  'To come and spoil the fun!'

The sea was wet as wet could be,
  The sands were dry as dry.
You could not see a cloud, because
  No cloud was in the sky:
No birds were flying overhead –
  There were no birds to fly.

The Walrus and the Carpenter
  Were walking close at hand:
They wept like anything to see
  Such quantities of sand:
'If this were only cleared away,'
  They said, 'it *would* be grand!'

'If seven maids with seven mops
  Swept it for half a year,
Do you suppose,' the Walrus said,
  'That they could get it clear?'
'I doubt it,' said the Carpenter,
  And shed a bitter tear.

'O Oysters, come and walk with us!'
  The Walrus did beseech.
'A pleasant walk, a pleasant talk,
  Along the briny beach:
We cannot do with more than four,
  To give a hand to each.'

The eldest Oyster looked at him,
  But never a word he said:
The eldest Oyster winked his eye,
  And shook his heavy head –
Meaning to say he did not choose
  To leave the oyster-bed.

But four young Oysters hurried up,
   All eager for the treat:
Their coats were brushed, their faces washed,
   Their shoes were clean and neat –
And this was odd, because, you know,
   They hadn't any feet.

Four other Oysters followed them,
   And yet another four;
And thick and fast they came at last,
   And more, and more, and more –
All hopping through the frothy waves,
   And scrambling to the shore.

The Walrus and the Carpenter
   Walked on a mile or so,
And then they rested on a rock
   Conveniently low:
And all the little Oysters stood
   And waited in a row.

'The time has come,' the Walrus said,
   'To talk of many things:
Of shoes – and ships – and sealing wax –
   Of cabbages – and kings –
And why the sea is boiling hot –
   And whether pigs have wings.'

'But wait a bit,' the Oysters cried,
    'Before we have our chat;
For some of us are out of breath,
    And all of us are fat!'
'No hurry!' said the Carpenter.
    They thanked him much for that.

'A loaf of bread,' the Walrus said,
    'Is what we chiefly need:
Pepper and vinegar besides
    Are very good indeed –
Now, if you're ready, Oysters dear,
    We can begin to feed.'

'But not on us!' the Oysters cried,
    Turning a little blue.
'After such kindness, that would be
    A dismal thing to do!'
'The night is fine,' the Walrus said,
    'Do you admire the view?

'It was so kind of you to come!
    And you are very nice!'
The Carpenter said nothing but
    'Cut us another slice!
I wish you were not quite so deaf –
    I've had to ask you twice!'

'It seems a shame,' the Walrus said,
  'To play them such a trick,
After we've brought them out so far,
  And made them trot so quick!'
The Carpenter said nothing but
  'The butter's spread too thick!'

'I weep for you,' the Walrus said:
  'I deeply sympathize.'
With sobs and tears he sorted out
  Those of the largest size,
Holding his pocket-handkerchief
  Before his streaming eyes.

'O Oysters,' said the Carpenter,
  'You've had a pleasant run!
Shall we be trotting home again!'
  But answer came there none –
And this was scarcely odd, because
  They'd eaten every one.

*Lewis Carroll*

## Wendy & Barry

Wendy wears her winter woollies,
Wendy's woollies keep her warm.
Barry boasts a bobbled beanie,
Barry's head is shaved and shorn.

Wendy wants a woolly beanie,
Wendy's mother's cut her hair,
Barry's always been a meanie.
Wendy says he doesn't care.

Barry's beanie's lost its bobble,
Barry shivers in the snow,
Wendy's sorry for his trouble,
Wendy's warm from head to toe.

Barry's taken off his beanie,
Barry's cold and getting colder,
Wendy says she'll marry Barry,
Wendy says, when they are older.

Barry with Wendy for a friend, he
Now goes beaniless but doesn't care.
Barry says he'll wait for Wendy.
Wendy says she'll grow her hair.

Barry's now no longer mean,
Barry dreams of being wed
And Wendy's happy to be seen
With Barry's beanie on her head.

*John Mole*

## *The Dragon in the Cellar*

There's a dragon!
There's a dragon!
There's a dragon in the cellar!
Yeah, we've got a cellar-dweller.
There's a dragon in the cellar.

He's a cleanliness fanatic,
Takes his trousers and his jacket
To the dragon from the attic
Who puts powder by the packet
In a preset automatic
With a rattle and a racket
That's disturbing and dramatic.

There's a dragon!
There's a dragon!
There's a dragon in the cellar!
With a flame that's red 'n' yeller.
There's a dragon in the cellar . . .

. . . and a dragon on the roof
Who's only partly waterproof,
So she's borrowed an umbrella
From the dragon in the cellar

There's a dragon!
There's a dragon!
There's a dragon in the cellar!
If you smell a panatella
It's the dragon in the cellar.

And the dragon from the study's
Helping out his cellar buddy,
Getting wet and soap-suddy
With the dragon from the loo
There to give a hand too,
While the dragon from the porch
Supervises with a torch.
Though the dragon from the landing,
Through a slight misunderstanding,
Is busy paint-stripping and sanding.

There's a dragon!
There's a dragon!
There's a dragon in the cellar!
Find my dad, and tell the feller
There's a dragon in the cellar . . .

. . . where the dragon from my room
Goes zoom, zoom, zoom
In a cloud of polish and spray-perfume,
Cos he's the dragon whom
They pay to brighten up the gloom
With a mop and a duster and a broom, broom, broom.

There's a dragon!
There's a dragon!
There's a dragon in the cellar!
Gonna get my mum and tell her
There's a dragon in the cellar.

*Nick Toczek*

## *Earth Songs*

Hear it in whisper
Morning mist
Drifting skeins of wool
Rising from water.

Hear it in squeaks, cries
Blather, jabber, prattle
Tumbling over each other
Chicks need feeding squawks.

Hear it in rumble, grumble
Pebbles pulled dragged
Wave after wave
Shuffle of shingle.

Hear it in madflap
Canvas in a gale
Angry wingbeats of heron
Rising from reeds.

Hear it in wind
Racing around tree tops
Blasting over fields
Bawling in your face.

Hear it in thunder
Bellowing around the valley.
Hear it in storming rain
Clamouring, howling . . .

Hear it in the mountains
The sea and the sky:
I am the earth
The earth
The earth.

*John Clarke*

## Doctor Bell

Doctor Bell fell down the well
And broke his collarbone.
Doctors should attend the sick
And leave the well alone.

*Anon.*

## Working for the Master
### (A Victorian Life in Service)

Jack do this, Jack do that
Clean the stair, shake the mat
Wash the dishes, polish the brass
Mop the floor, cut the grass
Dust the mantle, make the fire
Stand up straight, boy, higher, higher
Down to the kitchen and eat your bread
Then up the stairs and straight to bed.

*Richard Caley*

## Jamaican Clap Rhyme

Where your mamma gone?
She gone down town.

She take any money?
She take ten pound.

When your mamma come back,
what she gonna bring back?

Hats and frocks and
shoes and socks.

*Anon.*

## *You are old, Father William*

'You are old, Father William,' the young man said,
  'And your hair has become very white;
And yet you incessantly stand on your head –
  Do you think, at your age, it is right?'

'In my youth,' Father William replied to his son,
  'I feared it might injure the brain;
But, now that I'm perfectly sure I have none,
  Why, I do it again and again.'

'You are old,' said the youth, 'as I mentioned before,
  And have grown most uncommonly fat;
Yet you turned a back somersault in at the door –
  Pray, what is the reason of that?'

'In my youth,' said the sage, as he shook his grey locks,
    'I kept all my limbs very supple
By the use of this ointment – one shilling the box –
    Allow me to sell you a couple?'

'You are old,' said the youth, 'and your jaws are too weak
    For anything tougher than suet;
Yet you finished the goose, with the bones and the beak –
    Pray, how did you manage to do it?'

'In my youth,' said his father, 'I took to the law,
    And argued each case with my wife;
And the muscular strength, which it gave to my jaw,
    Has lasted the rest of my life.'

'You are old,' said the youth, 'one would hardly suppose
    That your eye was as steady as ever;
Yet you balanced an eel on the end of your nose –
    What made you so awfully clever?'

'I have answered three questions, and that is enough,'
    Said his father, 'Don't give yourself airs!
Do you think I can listen all day to such stuff?
    Be off, or I'll kick you downstairs!'

*Lewis Carroll*

## Down in the Valley

Down in the valley
  Where the green grass grows,
There stands *Daisy*,
  Washing out her clothes.
She sang and she sang
  And she sang so sweet,
She sang for her playmate
  Across the street.

Playmate, playmate.
  Will you come to tea?
Come next Saturday
  At half past three.
Tea, cakes, pancakes,
  All for you and me.
Won't we have a lovely time
  At half past three.

*Anon.*

## *I Bit an Apple . . .*

I bit an apple and the flesh was sweet:
Juice tingled on the tongue and from the fruit
Arose a scent that memory received
And in a flash raised ghosts of apple trees,
Leaves blistered with minutest bulbs of rain
Bewildering an autumn drawing room
Where carpets stained with unaccustomed shadow
Heard one old table creak, perhaps moved too
By some remembrance of a former time
When summer, like a lover, came to him
And laid amazing offerings at his feet.
I bit an apple and the spell was sweet.

*Vernon Scannell*

# What's Behind the Green Curtain?

'N*o! No! No!*'
That's our old headmaster going on and on
at morning assembly in the Hall.
Bored, I stare at the green curtain
hanging behind him on the wall
. . . and wonder
behind that green curtain
is there a non-smoking dragon with a code dinnis doze,
or a mini Mercurian with eyes on its toes? . . .

> '*In this school there'll be*
> *no fighting, no thumping,*
> *no punching, no clumping!*'

I wonder . . .
behind that green curtain
is there an ogre devouring an ox,
or a fox in a box, in a box, in a box? . . .

> '*In this school there'll be*
> *no kissing, no clouting,*
> *no kicking, no shouting!*'

I wonder . . .
behind that green curtain
is there a monster with worms on its face,
or simply an empty and echoing space? . . .

*'In this school there'll be*
*no running, no dreaming,*
*no spitting, no scream –!'*

When . . . suddenly, a hand,
a huge,
    hairy,
       horrible,
          horrendous hand appears,
grabs our old Headmaster
and hauls him behind the green curtain!
We gaze amazed, then realize he's gone,
he's gone . . . for certain!

He's gone!
No fuss. No mess.
We jump up, punch the air,
and shout, *'Yes!'*

# <u>'YESSSSSSSSSSS!!!'</u>

*Wes Magee*

# We Plough the Fields, and Scatter

We plough the fields, and scatter
The good seed on the land,
But it is fed and watered
By God's almighty hand;
He sends the snow in winter,
The warmth to swell the grain,
The breezes and the sunshine,
And soft refreshing rain:

*All good gifts around us*
*Are sent from heaven above;*
*Then thank the Lord, O thank the Lord,*
*For all His love.*

He only is the maker
Of all things near and far;
He paints the wayside flower;
He lights the evening star;
The winds and waves obey Him,
By Him the birds are fed;
Much more to us, His children,
He gives our daily bread:

We thank Thee then, O Father,
For all things bright and good,
The seed-time and the harvest,
Our life, our health, our food.
No gifts have we to offer
For all Thy love imparts,
But that which Thou desirest
Our humble, thankful hearts.

*Matthias Claudius*

## Grandpa's Glasses

Grandpa's lost his glasses.
Wherever can they be?

We've searched the floor,
Behind the door.

We've felt each stair,
His best armchair.

We've sifted bins
And rusty tins.

We've probed through boots
And ancient suits.

We've checked old socks
And even clocks.

We've combed the hedge
And garden veg.

We've scoured his shed
And under bed.

Then grandpa remembers –
They're still on his head!

*Jane Mann*

## *Genius*

I am a liric maniac
An Urban Oral GENIUS
My style iz fast 'n' FURIOUS
My manna iz SPONTANEOUS
My lirix make yer laugh sometimes
As well as bein SERIOUS
I'll send yer round 'n' round the bend
I'll make yer act DELIRIOUS
Each word is hot, and can't be held
I suppose you'd say I'm DANGEROUS
I know I have a way with wurdz
The wurd I'd use iz NOTORIOUS
For those who want to challenge me
I find it quite RIDICULOUS
When critics try and put me down
Can't see them, they're ANONYMOUS
The only thing I have ter say
I see them all as ODIOUS
I luv my rithmz 'n' the beatz
Smell my wurdz, they're ODOROUS
I love my lirix to the max
Evry syllable 'n' sound iz MARVELLOUS
I execute my wurdz so well
I suppose you'd call it MURDEROUS
To work so hard on all these wurdz

Some say it is LABORIOUS
There's double meaning in my style
Four syllables ter you. AM . . . BIG . . . U . . . OUS
I know I'm going on and on
But I certainly ain't MONOTONOUS
You have ter chill 'n' agree with me
The feeling is UNANIMOUS
Ter get inside yer head like this
I know that I am DEVIOUS
I do it in a sneaky way
I suppose I'd say MISCHIEVOUS
When pepul think about my rimez,
I know that they are CURIOUS
Don't understand the resun why
Becuz the cluez 'R' OBVIOUS
OK you're right, my wurdz 'R' good
I suppose they are MIRACULOUS
Astounded by this type of rime
I know you 'R' OBLIVIOUS
There'z only one thing left ter say
I'm bad 'n' cool
'N' INFAMOUS

*Martin Glynn*

# Thank You for the Harvest

Thank you for the sunshine
Thank you for the rain
Thank you that it's autumn
Harvest time again

Thank you for the seeds
Thank you for the roots
Thank you for the growth
Juicy shoots and fruits

Thank you for the sunshine
Thank you for the rain
Thank you that it's autumn
Harvest time again

Golden waving wheat
Golden ears of corn
Golden autumn sunshine
Glowing gold and warm

Thank you for the sunshine
Thank you for the rain
Thank you that it's autumn
Harvest time again

Apples red and juicy
Pears so crisp and green
Plums so plump and crimson
The ripest ever seen

*Thank you for the sunshine*
*Thank you for the rain*
*Thank you that it's autumn*
*Harvest time again*

Carrots and potatoes
Turnips, beans and peas
From the soil so rich and black
Nature gives us these

*Thank you for the sunshine*
*Thank you for the rain*
*Thank you that it's autumn*
*Harvest time again*

*Paul Cookson*

## *Wurd Up*

Blowin like a hurricane
Destroyin all the competishan
Kickin up the lirix hard
There ain't no opposishan
Coz
Wen I'm on a roll like this
I'm jus like a physishan
Like a boxer . . . punch you out
With lirical precishan
Flowin like a river
Jus
Flyin like a bird
'N'
Checkin out the ridim
Jus takin in my wurdz
It'z time
Ter climb
'n' rime
The sign
Jus growz
'n' flowz
'n' showz
'n' throwz

a skill
Ter thrill
'n' kill
Jus chill
Coz
I'm
Stingin like a nettle
Jus bitin like a flea
Smoother than a baby's skin
Much ruffer than the sea
Colder than an icicle
Hotta than the sun
Lirix always on the move
Like bullets from a gun
Much noizier than thunder
Much cooler than the rain
I'm fitta than an exercise
Deep within the brain
Sharpa than a needle
More solid than a rock
Repeatin like an echo
As rhythmic as a clock
More dangerus than a lion
Much louda than a plane
As quiet as a whisper
I burn yer like a flame
Fasta than a jaguar
Slowa than a snail
Yeah! rapid like a heartbeat
Tuffa than a nail

More painful than a scratch
As tasty as food
Horrible like a medicine
My lirix change yer mood
As tasty as a mango
As bitter as a lime
Softa than a coconut
Endless as the time
Kickin like a reggae song
Much sadda than the blues
I'm as tirin as a marathon
Give yer all the newz
Wilda than a stampede
As gentle as a breeze
Irritatin as a cough
More wicked than a sneeze
More lively than a child
Romantic that's me
Still harsh like the winter
Jus buzzin like a bee
The rimes 'n' times are signs
to blow 'n' show a flow

The wurdz

WURD UP!

*Martin Glynn*

# *Why Are You Late for School?*

I didn't get up
because I was too tired
and I was too tired
because I went to bed late
and I went to bed late
because I had homework
and I had homework
because the teacher made me
and the teacher made me
because I didn't understand
and I didn't understand
because I wasn't listening
and I wasn't listening
because I was staring out of the window
and I was staring out of the window
because I saw a cloud.
I am late, sir,
because I saw a cloud.

*Steve Turner*

## (You Ain't Nothing But A) Hedgehog

You ain't nothing but a hedgehog
Foragin' all the time
You ain't nothing but a hedgehog
Foragin' all the time
You ain't never pricked a predator
You ain't no porcupine.

*John Cooper Clarke*

## Ye Olde Pirate Drinking Song

One!
For a good ship with stout men on board
Two!
For a fair wind to take us abroad
Three!
For a crew who relish a fight
Four!
For a dark cove to hide in at night.

Five!
For a life of freedom and pleasure
Six!
For an island to bury our treasure
Seven!
For the maidens who wait in each port
Eight!
For the gallows which loom if we're caught.

*Chorus:*
With a Hey! and a Ho!
For a life spent at sea
You can try if you dare
But you'll never catch me.

*Richard Caley*

# The Cat from Down the Road

I am the cat from down the road.

*I am the cat from down the road.*
(neighbours call me James).

I *am the cat from down the road.*
*(neighbours call me James)*
and I've adopted all of you
from twenty-one to eighty-two
to give me milk and comfort too.

I *am the cat from down the road.*
*(neighbours call me James)*
*and I've adopted all of you*
*from twenty-one to eighty-two*
*to give me milk and comfort too.*
Stroke me. Call me pleasant names.

I *am the cat from down the road.*
*(neighbours call me James)*
*and I've adopted all of you*
*from twenty-one to eighty-two*
*to give me milk and comfort too.*
*Stroke me. Call me pleasant names.*
When your front door opens, I'm
always inside in record time.

I *am the cat from down the road.*
*(neighbours call me James)*
*and I've adopted all of you*
*from twenty-one to eighty-two*
*to give me milk and comfort too.*
*Stroke me. Call me pleasant names.*
*When your front door opens, I'm*
*always inside in record time.*
I mew and moan till the saucer comes.

I am the cat from down the road.
(neighbours call me James)
and I've adopted all of you
from twenty-one to eighty-two
to give me milk and comfort too.
Stroke me. Call me pleasant names.
When your front door opens, I'm
always inside in record time.
I mew and moan till the saucer comes.
I lap and stretch till the saucer comes.

I am the cat from down the road.
(neighbours call me James).

*Fred Sedgwick*

## *Tree and Leaf*

Said the tree to the leaf –
  Move over!
It's time for you
  to go.
There's winter round
  the corner
and somebody spoke
  of snow.
Under the frost's
  cold finger
my buds are growing
  fat.
The fires of spring
  are smouldering –
what do you think
  of that?

Said the leaf to the tree –
  I'm going!
It's time for me
  to fall . . .
I'm frail, and thin,
  and trembly . . .

I burn, like a golden
    ball.
I sing, with my silent
    beauty,
I float
    among streams of air,
and the living earth
    receives me
when oak and beech
    are bare.

*Jean Kenward*

## To the Virgins, to Make Much of Time

Gather ye rosebuds while ye may,
Old Time is still a-flying:
And this same flower that smiles to-day
To-morrow will be dying.

The glorious lamp of heaven, the sun,
The higher he's a-getting,
The sooner will his race be run,
And nearer he's to setting.

That age is best which is the first,
When youth and blood are warmer;
But being spent, the worse, and worst
Times still succeed the former.

Then be not coy, but use your time,
And while ye may, go marry:
For having lost but once your prime,
You may for ever tarry.

*Robert Herrick*

# October

## *Don't Look Round!*

I'm the door that squeaks
I'm the floorboard that creaks
I'm the voice in the night
That screams through your fright
I'm the tap on the pane
I'm the whisper of rain
Yes it's me on the stair
That's there and not there
That's there
and
not
there.

And wherever you go to
Be sure that I'll find you
I'm here, I'm there
I'm everywhere
My name is –
Behind You.

*Gareth Owen*

## Count-up to Planet Bed

I'm one for the window
and two for the door.

I'm three for the ceiling
and four for the floor.

I'm five for the morning
and six for the night.

I'm seven for the stairs
and eight for the light.

I'm nine for a story
and ten for my bed.

Now I'm off for a dream
to hold in my head.

*Katherine Gallagher*

# Whoops!

A million little dinosaurs
Having a good time
One fell over a cliff
And then there were
nine hundred and ninety-nine thousand,
nine hundred and ninety-nine.

Nine hundred and ninety-nine thousand,
nine hundred and ninety-nine dinosaurs
Having lots of fun
An asteroid hit the Earth
and then there were none.

*Roger Stevens*

# The Dragon Who Ate Our School

The day the dragon came to call,
She ate the gate, the playground wall
And, slate by slate, the roof and all,
The staffroom, gym and entrance hall,
And every classroom, big or small.

So . . .
She's undeniably great.
She's absolutely cool,
The dragon who ate
The dragon who ate
The dragon who ate our school.

Pupils panicked. Teachers ran.
She flew at them with wide wingspan.
She slew a few and then began
To chew through the lollipop man,
Two parked cars and a transit van.

Wow . . . !
She's undeniably great.
She's absolutely cool,
The dragon who ate
The dragon who ate
The dragon who ate our school.

She bit off the head of the head.
She said she was sad he was dead.
He bled and he bled and he bled.
And as she fed, her chin went red
And then she swallowed the cycle shed.

Oh . . .
She's undeniably great.
She's absolutely cool,
The dragon who ate
The dragon who ate
The dragon who ate our school.

It's thanks to her that we've been freed.
We needn't write. We needn't read.
Me and my mates are all agreed,
We're very pleased with her indeed.
So clear the way, let her proceed.

Cos . . .
She's undeniably great.
She's absolutely cool,
The dragon who ate
The dragon who ate
The dragon who ate our school.

There was some stuff she couldn't eat.
A monster forced to face defeat,
She spat it out along the street –
The dinner ladies' veg and meat
And that pink muck they serve for sweet.

But . . .
She's undeniably great.
She's absolutely cool,
The dragon who ate
The dragon who ate
The dragon who ate our school.

*Nick Toczek*

## *The Owl and the Pussy-cat*

### I

The Owl and the Pussy-cat went to sea
  In a beautiful pea-green boat,
They took some honey, and plenty of money,
  Wrapped up in a five-pound note.
The Owl looked up to the stars above,
  And sang to a small guitar,
'O lovely Pussy! O Pussy, my love,
  What a beautiful Pussy you are,
    You are,
    You are!
What a beautiful Pussy you are!'

## II

Pussy said to the Owl, 'You elegant fowl!
　　How charmingly sweet you sing!
O let us be married! too long we have tarried:
　　But what shall we do for a ring?'
They sailed away, for a year and a day,
　　To the land where the Bong-tree grows
And there in a wood a Piggy-wig stood
　　With a ring at the end of his nose,
　　　His nose,
　　　His nose,
　　With a ring at the end of his nose.

## III

'Dear Pig, are you willing to sell for one shilling
　　Your ring?' Said the Piggy, 'I will.'
So they took it away, and were married next day
　　By the Turkey who lives on the hill.
They dined on mince, and slices of quince,
　　Which they ate with a runcible spoon;
And hand in hand, on the edge of the sand,
　　They danced by the light of the moon,
　　　The moon,
　　　The moon,
　　They danced by the light of the moon.

*Edward Lear*

**6**

# *Ozymandias*

I met a traveller from an antique land
Who said: Two vast and trunkless legs of stone
Stand in the desert. Near them, on the sand,
Half sunk, a shattered visage lies, whose frown,
And wrinkled lip, and sneer of cold command
Tell that its sculptor well those passions read
Which yet survive (stamped on these lifeless things)
The hand that mocked them and the heart that fed:
And on the pedestal these words appear:
'My name is Ozymandias, King of Kings:
Look on my works, ye Mighty, and despair!'
Nothing beside remains. Round the decay
Of that colossal wreck, boundless and bare
The lone and level sands stretch far away.

*Percy Bysshe Shelley*

## *Lone Mission*

On evenings, after cocoa
(blackout down and sealed)
I would build plasticine Hamburgs
on green lino
and bomb them with encyclopedias
(dropped from ceiling level)
from my Lancaster Bomber
built
(usually)
from table, box and curtains
turret made of chairs
radio and gas masks
tray and kitchen ware
But:
Aircrew were my problem
gunners mid and rear
radio and bomber
nav and engineer.

Each night I flew lone missions
through flak both hot and wild
and learned it wasn't easy
to be an only child.

*Peter Dixon*

## *Golden Slumbers Kiss Your Eyes*

Golden slumbers kiss your eyes,
Smiles awake you when you rise.
Sleep, pretty wantons, do not cry,
And I will sing a lullaby:
Rock them, rock them, lullaby.

Care is heavy, therefore sleep you;
You are care, and care must keep you.
Sleep, pretty wantons, do not cry,
And I will sing a lullaby:
Rock them, rock them, lullaby.

*Thomas Dekker*

## *My Rocket Dreamed . . .*

My rocket dreamed of circling the earth,
orbiting the moon,
zigzagging planets,
looping the loop with satellites,
dodging meteorites,
racing comets
and disappearing into time warps and black holes.

Instead, it circled the garden shed,
orbited the swing,
zigzagged the apple tree,
looped the loop with the clothes line,
dodged two butterflies,
raced one wasp and a bluebottle
then disappeared over the hedge
into the time warp and black hole
that is Mr Hislop's back garden.

*Paul Cookson*

## *If*

If you can keep your head when all about you
Are losing theirs and blaming it on you,
If you can trust yourself when all men doubt you,
But make allowance for their doubting too;
If you can wait and not be tired of waiting,
Or being lied about, don't deal in lies,
Or being hated, don't give way to hating,
And yet don't look too good, nor talk too wise:

If you can dream – and not make dreams your master;
If you can think – and not make thoughts your aim;
If you can meet with Triumph and Disaster
And treat those two impostors just the same;
If you can bear to hear the truth you've spoken
Twisted by knaves to make a trap for fools,
Or watch the things you gave your life to, broken,
And stoop and build 'em up with worn-out tools:

If you can make one heap of all your winnings
And risk it on one turn of pitch-and-toss,
And lose, and start again at your beginnings
And never breathe a word about your loss;
If you can force your heart and nerve and sinew
To serve your turn long after they are gone,
And so hold on when there is nothing in you
Except the Will which says to them: 'Hold on!'

If you can talk with crowds and keep your virtue,
Or walk with Kings – nor lose the common touch,
If neither foes nor loving friends can hurt you,
If all men count with you, but none too much;
If you can fill the unforgiving minute
With sixty seconds' worth of distance run,
Yours is the Earth and everything that's in it,
And – which is more – you'll be a Man, my son!

*Rudyard Kipling*

**11**

## *Castle to be Built in the Woods*

Choose a wood.

Make a clearing
near a stream.

Dig a moat.
Make it deep, wide.
Fill it with water. One bridge only.

Lay solid foundations for your castle.
Then build strong buttresses, stout keeps
and tall towers with crenellations
around the high battlements.

Make sure your castle has servants such as
clerks, tailors, nurses, messengers,
damsels, brewers, and a barber.
You will need to lay down stores
of food, wine, wax, spices and herbs.

An airy church inside the castle grounds
and a dark dungeon deep below ground
will mean that you can have
Heaven and Hell at your fingertips.
Don't forget to stock your arsenal with
swords, daggers, lances, shields, battle-axes, etc.

Fire arrows at anyone who tries to
attack your castle. Build murder-holes
so that you can drop missiles and stones
on the heads of your enemies.
If you catch spies, lock them in
the smallest, narrowest, smelliest room.
Act ruthlessly. Behead people, frequently.

Hide treasure in a very secret part of the castle.
Lock a beautiful princess in the tower.
Force your fiercest dragon to guard both of these.
Nominate a knight who will fight your battles
so that you are never injured or endangered.
Employ a storyteller to make up tall tales
and ghost stories about your castle.
Marry someone and he can be the king.

*John Rice*

## *I Would Win the Gold If These Were Olympic Sports . . .*

Bubblegum blowing
Goggle box watching
Late morning snoring
Homework botching

Quilt ruffling
Little brother teasing
Pizza demolishing
Big toe cheesing

Insult hurling, wobbly throwing
Infinite blue belly button fluff growing

Late night endurance computer screen gazing
Non-attentive open-jawed eyeball glazing

Ultimate volume decibel blaring
Long-distance marathon same sock wearing

Recognize all these as sports then meet . . .
Me! The Champ Apathetic Athlete!

*Paul Cookson*

## *The Shapeshifter's Riddle*

I am the cat that leaps in my lap
I am the grey mouse caught in a trap
I am the yawn at the end of the day
I am the love that would love Spring to stay.

I am the hurt of the knee that is cut
I am the door that is open or shut
I am the longing to see the sun rise
I am the joy in the vast starry skies.

I am the oak branch      I am the bird
I am the paper           I am the word
I am the child           I am the man
I am the bridge          I am the span

I am older               Never old
I am bolder              Never bold
I am crying              Now I smile
I am an inch             I am a mile
I am a day               I am a night
I am the darkness        I am the light
I am a minute            I am a year
I am arriving            Not quite here
I am becoming            Always try
So pray then             Tell me
Who am                   I?

*Stephen Bowkett*

## The Schoolkids' Rap

Miss was at the blackboard writing with the chalk,
When suddenly she stopped in the middle of her talk.
She snapped her fingers – snap! snap! snap!
Pay attention, children, and I'll teach you how to rap.

She picked up a pencil, she started to tap.
All together, children, now, clap! clap! clap!
Just get the rhythm, just get the beat.
Drum it with your fingers, stamp it with your feet.

That's right, children, keep in time.
Now we've got the rhythm, all we need is the rhyme.
This school is cool. Miss Grace is ace.
Strut your stuff with a smile on your face.

Snap those fingers, tap those toes.
Do it like they do it on the video shows.
Flap it! Slap it! Clap! Snap! Clap!
Let's all do the schoolkids' rap!

*John Foster*

# *A Smile*

Smiling is infectious,
you catch it like the flu.
When someone smiled at me today
I started smiling too.

I passed around the corner
and someone saw my grin.
When he smiled, I realized
I'd passed it on to him.

I thought about my smile and then
I realized its worth.
A single smile like mine could travel
right around the earth.

If you feel a smile begin
don't leave it undetected.
Let's start an epidemic quick
and get the world infected.

*Jez Alborough*

## *Fairground Attraction*

I knew she was the one for me
The moment I saw her

My heart looped the loop
And helter-skeltered ever faster

But I was like the coconut.
Shy.

*Paul Cookson*

## *The Kraken*

Below the thunders of the upper deep,
Far, far beneath in the abysmal sea,
His ancient, dreamless, uninvaded sleep
The Kraken sleepeth: faintest sunlights flee
About his shadowy sides; above him swell
Huge sponges of millennial growth and height;
And far away into the sickly light,
From many a wondrous grot and secret cell
Unnumber'd and enormous polypi
Winnow with giant arms the slumbering green.
There hath he lain for ages, and will lie
Battening upon huge sea-worms in his sleep,
Until the latter fire shall heat the deep;
Then once by man and angels to be seen,
In roaring he shall rise and on the surface die.

*Alfred, Lord Tennyson*

# I Can Count
### (To share with younger brothers and sisters)

I can count to one
With a currant bun.
> *(put imaginary bun in mouth and loudly munch)*

I can count to two
With me and you.
> *(point to self, then someone else)*

I can count to three
Bumble-bee.
> *(flap hands at shoulder-level, like wings)*

I can count to four
Give a loud ROAR.
> *(pronounce ROAR as a long, loud growl)*

I can count to five
Watch me drive.
> *(hands to mime turning a steering-wheel)*

I can count to six
Juggling tricks.
> *(hands to mime juggling with balls or clubs)*

I can count to seven
Point to Heaven.

*(pointing upwards)*

I can count to eight
Concentrate.

*(hunched up, with one fist against forehead)*

I can count to nine
Do the happy sign.

*(thumbs up)*

I can count to ten
Let's do that again . . .

*(holding up all ten fingers and thumbs)*

I can count to one
With a currant bun.

*(put imaginary bun in mouth and loudly munch)*

I can count to two
With me and you.

*(point to self, then someone else)*

I can count to three
Bumble-bee.

*(flap hands at shoulder-level, like wings)*

I can count to four
Give a loud ROAR.

*(pronounce ROAR as a long, loud growl)*

403

I can count to five
Watch me drive.

> *(hands to mime turning a steering-wheel)*

I can count to six
Juggling tricks.

> *(hands to mime juggling with balls or clubs)*

I can count to seven
Point to Heaven.

> *(pointing upwards)*

I can count to eight
Concentrate.

> *(hunched up, with one fist against forehead)*

I can count to nine
Do the happy sign.

> *(thumbs up)*

I can count to ten

> *(holding up all ten fingers and thumbs)*

Thank you, ladies and gentlemen.

> *(bowing slowly and grandly)*

*Nick Toczek*

# *I'm Special!*

In our school
  I'm the only one
  who can zip around
  the playground
  at thirty miles an hour!
Watch out everyone. My
wheelchair is supercharged –
I'm special!

In our school
  I'm the only one
  whose fingers know
  how you look, who
  never stumbles in the dark.
My eyes are in my fingertips,
my ears pick up every sound –
  I'm special!

In our school
  I'm the only one
  who can switch off
  our teacher's voice
  when I've had enough.
Sometimes I can listen in
to staffroom conversation –
  I'm special!

In our school
 I'm the only one
 who knows the names
 of all the birds
 along the riverbank.
I can't write them down,
but I can mimic every call –
 I'm special!

In our school
 I'm the only one
 of me. No one else
 thinks the same, speaks
 or looks the same.
In all the world, I'm the only me.
Amazing, when you think of it –
 I'm special!

*Moira Andrew*

## *Haircut Rap*

Ah sey, ah want it short,
Short back an' side,
Ah tell him man, ah tell him
When ah teck him aside,
Ah sey, ah want a haircut
Ah can wear with pride,
So lef' it long on top
But short back an' side.

Ah sey try an' put a pattern
In the shorter part,
Yuh could put a skull an' crossbone,
Or an arrow through a heart,
Meck sure ah have enough hair lef'
Fe cover me wart,
Lef a likkle pon the top,
But the res' – keep it short.

Well, bwoy, him start to cut
An' me settle down to wait,
Him was cuttin' from seven
Till half past eight,
Ah was startin' to get worried
Cos ah see it gettin' late,
But then him put the scissors down
Sey 'There yuh are, mate.'

407

Well ah did see a skull an a
Criss-cross bone or two,
But was me own skull an bone
That was peepin' through,
Ah look jus' like a monkey
Ah did see once at the zoo,
Him sey, 'What's de matter, Tammy,
Don't yuh like the hair-do?'

Well, ah feel me heart stop beatin'
When me look pon me reflection,
Ah feel like somet'ing frizzle up
Right in me middle section
Ah look aroun' fe somewhey
Ah could crawl into an' hide
The day ah mek me brother cut
Me hair short back an' side.

*Valerie Bloom*

# When that I was and a little tiny boy

When that I was and a little tiny boy,
  With hey, ho, the wind and the rain;
A foolish thing was but a toy,
  For the rain it raineth every day.

But when I came to man's estate,
  With hey, ho, the wind and the rain;
'Gainst knaves and thieves men shut their gates,
  For the rain it raineth every day.

But when I came, alas! to wive,
  With hey, ho, the wind and the rain;
By swaggering could I never thrive,
  For the rain it raineth every day.

But when I came unto my beds,
  With hey, ho, the wind and the rain;
With toss-pots still had drunken heads,
  For the rain it raineth every day.

A great while ago the world begun,
  With hey, ho, the wind and the rain;
But that's all one, our play is done,
  And we strive to please you every day.

*William Shakespeare*

## *My Gran*

My Gran is
    a giggle-in-the-corner-like-a-child
        kind of Gran

She is
    a put-your-cold-hand-in-my-pocket
    a keep-your-baby-curls-in-my-locket
        kind of Gran

She is
    a make-it-better-with-a-treacle-toffee
    a what-you-need's-a-cup-of-milky-coffee
    a hurry-home-I-love-you-awfully
        kind of Gran

She is
    a butter-ball-for-your-bad-throat
    a stitch-your-doll-a-new-green-coat
    a let's-make-soapy-bubbles-float
    a hold-my-hand-I'm-seasick-in-a-boat
        kind of Gran

She is

a toast-your-tootsies-by-the-fire
a crack-the-wishbone-for-your-heart's-desire
a ladies-don't-sweat-they-perspire
a funny-old-fashioned-higgledy-piggledy-lady-to-admire

kind of Gran

And this lovely grandmother
is mine, all mine!

*Moira Andrew*

## Windy Nights

Whenever the moon and stars are set,
   Whenever the wind is high,
All night long in the dark and wet,
   A man goes riding by.
Late in the night when the fires are out,
Why does he gallop and gallop about?

Whenever the trees are crying aloud,
　And ships are tossed at sea,
By, on the highway, low and loud,
　By at the gallop goes he.
By at the gallop he goes, and then
By he comes back at the gallop again.

*Robert Louis Stevenson*

## *Dazzledance*
### *(for Heather)*

I have an eye of silver,
I have an eye of gold,
I have a tongue of reed-grass
　and a story to be told.

I have a hand of metal,
I have a hand of clay,
I have two arms of granite,
　and a song for every day.

I have a foot of damson,
I have a foot of corn,
I have two legs of leaf-stalk
   and a dance as yet unborn.

I have a dream of water,
I have a dream of snow,
I have a thought of wildfire
   and a harp-string long and low.

I have an eye of silver,
I have an eye of gold,
I have a tongue of reed-grass
   and a story to be told.

*John Rice*

## *The Most Important Rap*

I am an astronaut
I circle the stars
I walk on the moon
I travel to Mars
I'm brave and tall
There is nothing I fear
And I am the most important person here.

I am a teacher
I taught you it all
I taught you why your
spaceship doesn't fall
If you couldn't read or write
where would you be?
The most important person here is me.

Who are you kidding?
Are you taking the mick?
Who makes you better
when you're feeling sick?
I am a doctor
and I'm always on call
and I am more important than you all.

But I'm your mother
Don't forget me
If it wasn't for your mother
where would you be?
I washed your nappies
and changed your vest
I'm the most important
and Mummy knows best.

I am a child
and the future I see
and there'd be no future
if it wasn't for me
I hold the safety
of the planet in my hand
I'm the most important
and you'd better understand.

Now just hold on
I've a message for you all
Together we stand
and divided we fall
so let's make a circle
and all remember this
Who's the most important?

EVERYBODY IS!

*Roger Stevens*

## *In Flanders Fields*

In Flanders fields the poppies blow
Between the crosses, row on row,
 That mark our place; and in the sky
 The larks, still bravely singing, fly
Scarce heard amid the guns below.

We are the Dead. Short days ago
We lived, felt dawn, saw sunset glow,
 Loved and were loved, and now we lie
 In Flanders fields.

Take up our quarrel with the foe:
To you from failing hands we throw
   The torch; be yours to hold it high.
   If ye break faith with us who die
We shall not sleep, though poppies grow
   In Flanders fields.

*John McCrae*

# Nineteen Things to Do in Winter

Find the sledge in the back of the garage
   grease the runners and paint it red
Watch the weather report for news of snow.
Snuggle up in bed and read a book
   that's as long as a long winter night.
Listen to the wind moan
Keep an eye on the sky for snow clouds on the horizon
Draw rude faces on steamed-up windows
Go to football. Watch the Gunners. Groan and cheer
Rescue fish in frozen ponds
   and old ladies at the bottom of icy hills
Drop an icicle down your sister's tights
Warm cold knees and icy bottom around roaring fire

Check the sky for snow

Fit sledge with seats made from cushions of armchair in
 front room

Make balls of fat and birdseed to feed the blue tits

Be sympathetic when Dad fuses the lights

Ring the meteorological office and ask when it's going to
 snow

Paint go-faster stripes on sledge

Say to Mum, I've no idea where the armchair cushions
 have gone

Dream of green trees and buzzing bees and summer seas

Wonder why it hasn't snowed again this year

*Roger Stevens*

## From a Railway Carriage

Faster than fairies, faster than witches,
Bridges and houses, hedges and ditches;
And charging along like troops in a battle,
All through the meadows the horses and cattle:
All of the sights of the hill and the plain
Fly as thick as driving rain;
And ever again, in the wink of an eye,
Painted stations whistle by.

Here is a child who clambers and scrambles,
All by himself and gathering brambles;
Here is a tramp who stands and gazes;
And there is the green for stringing the daisies!
Here is a cart run away in the road
Lumping along with man and load;
And here is a mill, and there is a river:
Each a glimpse and gone for ever!

*Robert Louis Stevenson*

## Shadows

Shadows shiver in the twilight,
shadows gather in the gloom,
shadows slink across the ceiling,
shadows seep into my room.

They're creeping into corners,
they're oozing through the door,
they're writhing on the window,
they're squirming on the floor.

418

Shadows drifting, shadows shifting,
shadows swarming overhead,
shadows looming, shadows lurking,
shadows prowling round my bed.

Shadows flock like hungry vultures
watching day die into night,
shadows waiting for the moment
when I turn out the light . . .

*Jane Clarke*

## *Witches' Song from* Macbeth

Round about the cauldron go;
In the poison'd entrails throw.
Toad, that under cold stone
Days and nights has thirty-one
Swelter'd venom, sleeping got,
Boil thou first i'th'charmed pot.
Double, double toil and trouble:
Fire, burn; and cauldron, bubble.
Fillet of a fenny snake,

In the cauldron boil and bake;
Eye of newt, and toe of frog,
Wool of bat, and tongue of dog,
Adder's fork, and blind-worm's sting,
Lizard's leg, and howlet's wing.
For a charm of powerful trouble,
Like a hell-broth boil and bubble.
Double, double toil and trouble:
Fire, burn; and cauldron, bubble.

*William Shakespeare*

## *Halloween Poem*
### *(A poem for voices)*

Trick or treat! Trick or treat!
In a sheet. Trick or treat!

Trick or treat! Trick or treat!
Up the street and down the street,
In a sheet. Trick or treat!

Trick or treat! Trick or treat!
Hear the beat of running feet
Up the street and down the street
In a sheet. Trick or treat!

Trick or treat! Trick or treat!
Stuff to spend or stuff to eat.
Hear the beat of running feet
Up the street and down the street
In a sheet. Trick or treat!

Trick or treat! Trick or treat!
Sour or sweet? We repeat,
Stuff to spend or stuff to eat.
Hear the beat of running feet
Up the street and down the street
In a sheet. Trick or treat!

Trick or treat! Trick or treat!
Don't care who we meet.
Sour or sweet? We repeat,
Stuff to spend or stuff to eat.
Hear the beat of running feet
Up the street and down the street
In a sheet. Trick or treat!

Trick or treat! Trick or treat!
Wind! Rain! Hail! Sleet!
Don't care who we meet.
Sour or sweet? We repeat,
Stuff to spend or stuff to eat.
Hear the beat of running feet
Up the street and down the street
In a sheet. Trick or treat!

*John Whitworth*

# November

## No!

No sun – no moon!
No morn – no noon –
No dawn – no dusk – no proper time of day –
No sky – no earthly view –
No distance looking blue –
No road – no street – no 't'other side the way' –
No end to any Row –
No indications where the Crescents go –
No top to any steeple –
No recognitions of familiar people –
No courtesies for showing 'em –
No knowing 'em –
No travelling at all – no locomotion,
No inkling of the way – no notion –
'No go' – by land or ocean –
No mail – no post –
No news from any foreign coast –

No Park – no Ring – no afternoon gentility –
   No company – no nobility –
No warmth, no cheerfulness, no healthful ease,
  No comfortable feel in any member –
No shade, no shine, no butterflies, no bees,
  No fruits, no flowers, no leaves, no birds, –
    November!

                       *Thomas Hood*

## Things to Remember

The buttercups in May,
The wild rose on the spray,
The poppy in the hay,

The primrose in the dell,
The freckled foxglove bell,
The honeysuckle's smell

Are things I would remember
When cheerless, raw November
Makes room for dark December.

                   *James Reeves*

## *Tick-tock*

Time's a tick
A-tock
A-tick
A ghost
That burns
The candle wick.
That lets
A life
Fill up
With light,
That measures
Sunshine's
Hours
Flight
Then all
Too soon
Tick-took
Goodnight!   Goodnight!   Goodnight!

Goodnight!

*Ian Larmont*

## Todd the Backyard King

*(A poem to read aloud – remember to
miaow sweetly at the end)*

I'm not your fluffy lap-cat
Who purrs to hear you sing;
Your curl-up-on-the-mat-cat
With dainty bell to ring;
Your pretty-pounce-and-pat-cat
Who chases after string . . .
I'm Todd, the catch-a-rat-cat,
The Mighty Backyard King.

I'm not your snooze-and-yawn-cat
With soft and velvet paw;
Your doze-upon-the-lawn-cat
With sheathed and secret claw;
Your slink-about-and-fawn-cat
With meek and milky jaw . . .
I'm Todd, the blood-at-dawn-cat,
Who takes his breakfast RAW.

I'm not your prize-rosette-cat
(My whiskers fray and bend);
I'm not your matching-set-cat
(One ear has lost its end);
I'm not your preen-and-pet-cat
(My coat's too torn to mend) . . .
But when I'm cold-and-wet-cat;
I'm Todd – your fireside friend.

*Clare Bevan*

## *The Biggest Firework*

The biggest firework
Ever lit,
Fizzed, banged,
Glittered, flew
In Golden-Silver-
Red-Green-Blue.
It rocketed
So far away,
It brought to night
A burst of day,
Electric bulbs
A million bright
Of shining spray.

But of its fiery magic spell
All that is left
Is the smoke smell . . .

*Anon.*

# A Message to My Sister

The spider in the bath
has spent all night trying to get out,
and *you* scream.

*Judith Green*

# The Horrible House on Haunted Hill

There's a horrible house on Haunted Hill (Wooo-eeeee!)
The freezing winds blow cold and chill (Brrrrrrrrrrrr!)
The rickety roof has sprung a leak (drip, drop, drip, drop)
The rotting floorboards groan and creak (Creeeeeek!)
And bumbling bats fly through the air (Flappety flap!
  Flapetty flap!)
The doors go bang when there's no one there (Bang!
  Bang!)
A warty witch in a pointy hat (ha! ha! ha! ha!)
Lives up there with a sinister cat (Miaow! Ptht!)
A rattling skeleton bangs his bones (Clickety clack, clickety
  clack)
A gibbering ghost just moans and groans (Oooh! Me
  back!)
And now I've said all I can say
I hope you're going to stay away from the

| | |
|---|---|
| Horrible house | (woo-ee) |
| And the horrible winds | (brrrrrrrr) |
| And the horrible roof | (drip drop) |
| And the horrible boards | (creeeak) |
| The horrible bats | (flappety flap) |
| The horrible doors | (bang! bang) |

The horrible witch        (ha ha, ha ha)
The horrible cat          (miaow, ptht!)
The horrible skeleton    (clickety clack)
And the horrible ghost    (oooh, me back!)

The horrible house on Haunted Hill
Was haunted then and it's haunted still!

*(General outbreak of scary noises!)*

*Kaye Umansky*

# I Had a Nickel

I had a nickel and I walked around the block.
I walked right into a baker shop.
I took two doughnuts right out of the grease;
I handed the lady my five-cent piece.
She looked at the nickel and she looked at me,
And said, 'This money's no good to me.
There's a hole in the nickel, and it goes right through.'
Says I, 'There's a hole in the doughnut, too.'

*Anon.*

# Barry and Beryl the Bubblegum Blowers

Barry and Beryl the bubblegum blowers
blew bubblegum bubbles as big as balloons.
All shapes and sizes, zebras and zeppelins,
swordfish and sea lions, sharks and baboons,
babies and buckets, bottles and biplanes,
buffaloes, bees, trombones and bassoons
Barry and Beryl the bubblegum blowers
blew bubblegum bubbles as big as balloons.

Barry and Beryl the bubblegum blowers
blew bubblegum bubbles all over the place.
Big ones in bed, on back seats of buses,
blowing their bubbles in baths with bad taste,
they blew and they bubbled from breakfast till bedtime
the biggest gum bubble that history traced.
One last big breath . . . and the bubble exploded
bursting and blasting their heads into space.
Yes, Barry and Beryl the bubblegum blowers
blew bubbles that blasted their heads into space.

*Paul Cookson*

## Rosy Apple

Rosy apple, lemon and a pear,
A bunch of roses she shall wear,
A sword and pistol by her side,
She shall be a bride.
Take her by the lily-white hand,
Lead her across the water.
Blow her a kiss and say goodbye –
For she's the captain's daughter.

*Anon.*

## They Shall Not Grow Old

With proud thanksgiving, a mother for her children,
England mourns for her dead across the sea.
Flesh of her flesh they were, spirit of her spirit,
Fallen in the cause of the free.

Solemn the drums thrill; Death august and royal
Sings sorrow up into immortal spheres.
There is music in the midst of desolation
And a glory that shines upon our tears.

They went with songs to the battle, they were young,
Straight of limb, true of eye, steady and aglow.
They were staunch to the end against odds uncounted,
They fell with their faces to the foe.

They shall grow not old, as we who are left grow old:
Age shall not weary them, nor the years condemn.
At the going down of the sun and in the morning
We shall remember them.

They mingle not with their laughing comrades again;
They sit no more at familiar tables of home;
They have no lot in our labour of the day-time;
They sleep beyond England's foam.

But where our desires are and our hopes profound,
Felt as a well-spring that is hidden from sight,
To the innermost heart of their own land they are known
As the stars are known to the Night;

As the stars that shall be bright when we are dust,
Moving in marches upon the heavenly plain,
As the stars that are starry in the time of our darkness,
To the end, to the end, they remain.

*Laurence Binyon*

## *Patchwork Rap*

I'm a touch lazy
Don't like doing much work
But I often get the itch
To pitch into some patchwork
It may be a hotchpotch
Like fretwork or such work
When I slouch on my couch
And I fetch out my patchwork
First I snatch a patch
From the batch in my pouch
But the patch doesn't match
The patches on my patchwork
So I catch another patch
From the batch in my satchel
And this one matches
The patches on my patchwork.
So I take my patch
And attach it with stitches
Patch against patch

434

Where the patchwork matches
But if it doesn't match
Even after it's attached
Then the mismatched stitch
Has to be detached.

I don't like thatchwork
Don't like ditchwork
Only kind I favour
Is my patchwork stitchwork
And soon my patchwork's
Going like clockwork
Sharper than a pitchfork
Neater than brickwork
Hotter than a firework
Cooler than a waxwork.
So I snatch a patch
From the batch in my pouch
But the patch doesn't match
The patches on my patchwork
So I catch another patch
From the batch in my satchel
And this one matches
The patches on my patchwork.
So I take my patch
And attach it with stitches
Patch against patch
Where the patchwork matches
And I keep on patching
Till everything's matching
And I keep on stitching

Till I've filled up the kitchen
With my rich rich rich
Wider than a soccer pitch
Wonderful colourful patchwork quilt!
Now which stitch is which?

                              *Adrian Mitchell*

## *La Belle Dame sans Merci*

O, what can ail thee, knight at arms,
  Alone and palely loitering?
The sedge has withered from the lake,
  And no birds sing.

O, what can ail thee, knight at arms,
  So haggard and so woe-begone?
The squirrel's granary is full,
  And the harvest's done.

I see a lily on thy brow
  With anguish moist and fever-dew,
And on thy cheeks a fading rose
  Fast withereth too.

I met a lady in the meads,
    Full beautiful – a faery's child,
Her hair was long, her foot was light,
    And her eyes were wild.

I made a garland for her head,
    And bracelets too, and fragrant zone,
She looked at me as she did love,
    And made sweet moan.

I set her on my pacing steed
    And nothing else saw all day long;
For sideways would she lean, and sing
    A faery's song.

She found me roots of relish sweet,
    And honey wild and manna dew;
And sure in language strange she said –
    I love thee true.

She took me to her elfin grot,
    And there she gazed and sighed full sore:
And there I shut her wild, wild eyes
    With kisses four.

And there she lullèd me asleep,
    And there I dreamed, ah woe betide,
The latest dream I ever dreamed
    On a cold hill side.

I saw pale kings and princes too,
    Pale warriors, death-pale were they all:
They cry'd – 'La Belle Dame sans Merci
    Hath thee in thrall!'

I saw their starved lips in the gloom
    With horrid warning gapèd wide,
And I awoke, and found me here
    On the cold hill side.

And this is why I sojourn here
    Alone and palely loitering,
Though the sedge is withered from the lake,
    And no birds sing.

*John Keats*

## *November Night*

Listen . . .
With faint dry sound,
Like steps of passing ghosts,
The leaves, frost-crisp'd, break from the trees
And fall.

*Adelaide Crapsey*

# *Baby Rap!*

Adults go gooey with a baby on their lap,
it's the cootchy-coo, cuddly-poo baby rap.

    Woopsy, poopsy, honey bun,
    sweetie, tweetie, sugar plum,
    snuggums, diddums, cutesie tootsie,
    bunnikins, honeykins, footsie wootsie.

Out on the street adults push their buggies,
desperate for coos and lots of huggies
when baby cries; time to change that nap,
parents smile for it's their time to rap!

    Woopsy, poopsy, honey bun,
    sweetie, tweetie, sugar plum,
    snuggums, diddums, cutesie tootsie,
    bunnikins, honeykins, footsie wootsie.

Adults enjoy being a patter chatterbox
with 'precious, izzums, bless your cotton socks.'
So when babies cry, 'daddeeee, mummeeee,'
all adults do is shove in a dummy!

Woopsy, poopsy, honey bun,
sweetie, tweetie, sugar plum,
snuggums, diddums, cutesie tootsie,
bunnikins, honeykins, footsie wootsie.

Babies must wonder what's happening here,
all this cooey talk dribbling in their ear.
Those adults so noisy and full of prattle
perhaps their mouths should be stuffed with a RATTLE!

Woopsy, poopsy, honey bun,
sweetie, tweetie, sugar plum,
snuggums, diddums, cutesie tootsie,
bunnikins, honeykins, footsie wootsie.

Adults go gooey with a baby on their lap,
it's the cootchy-coo, cuddly-poo baby rap!

*Ian Souter*

## *Conversation Piece*

Late again Blenkinsop?
What's the excuse this time?
*Not my fault sir.*
Whose fault is it then?
*Grandma's sir.*
Grandma's. What did she do?
*She died sir.*
Died?
*She's seriously dead all right sir.*
That makes four grandmothers this term
And all on PE days Blenkinsop.
*I know. It's very upsetting sir.*
How many grandmothers have you got Blenkinsop?
*Grandmothers sir? None sir.*
None?
*All dead sir.*
And what about yesterday Blenkinsop?
*What about yesterday sir?*
You missed maths.
*That was the dentist sir.*
The dentist died?
*No sir. My teeth sir.*
You missed the test Blenkinsop.
*I'd been looking forward to it too sir.*

Right, line up for PE.
*Can't sir.*
No such word as can't. Why can't you?
*No kit sir.*
Where is it?
*Home sir.*
What's it doing at home?
*Not ironed sir.*
Couldn't you iron it?
*Can't do it sir.*
Why not?
*My hand sir.*
Who usually does it?
*Grandma sir.*
Why couldn't she do it?
*Dead sir.*

*Gareth Owen*

## The Night Is Darkening Round Me

The night is darkening round me,
The wild winds coldly blow;
But a tyrant spell has bound me
And I cannot, cannot go.

The giant trees are bending
Their bare boughs weighed with snow.
And the storm is fast descending,
And yet I cannot go.

Clouds beyond clouds above me,
Wastes beyond wastes below;
But nothing drear can move me;
I will not, cannot go.

*Emily Brontë*

## *In Praise of Aunties*

An aunt
is a tender plant.
You really can't
be too fond of an aunt.

*Judith Nicholls*

## *First Star*

Starlight, starbright,
First star that I see tonight:
From Earth, fantastically far,
I make my wishes on a star.

I wish for a world at peace
Where wars and hatred cease.
I wish for a world that's fair
Whose people give and share.
I wish for a world that's clean:
Cared-for, unspoilt, green.
I wish my life to be,
With friends and family,
Loyal, loving, caring,
Adventurous and daring.

On the first star of the night,
Go wishes, go, take flight.

*Eric Finney*

## *The Hippopotamus*

Consider the poor hippopotamus:
His life is unduly monotonous.
He lives half asleep
At the edge of the deep,
And his face is as big as his bottom is.

*Anon.*

# *Question Time*

*W*hat does a monster look like?
Well . . . hairy and scary,
　　and furry and burly
　　　　and pimply and dimply
　　　　　　and warty
　　　　　　　　and naughty
　　　　　　　　　　and wrinkled and crinkled . . .
That's what a monster looks like.

*How does a monster move?*
It oozes.
　　It shambles.
　　　　It crawls and it ambles.
　　　　　　It slouches and shuffles
　　　　　　　　and trudges.
It lumbers and waddles,
　　it creeps and it toddles . . .
That's how a monster moves.

*Where does a monster live?*
In garden sheds,
　　under beds,
　　　　in wardrobes,
　　　　　　in plug holes,

446

in ditches.
Beneath city streets,
just under your feet . . .
That's where a monster lives.

*How does a monster eat?*
It slurps
and it burps.
It gobbles and gulps.
It sips and it swallows
and scoffs.
It nibbles and munches.
It chews and it crunches.
That's how a monster eats.

*What does a monster eat?*
Slugs.
And bats.
And bugs
and rats.
And stones and mud
and bones and blood.
And squelchy squids . . .
and nosy kids.
YUM!
That's what a monster eats!

*Michaela Morgan*

## Careful With That, You Might Break It

See what I've found.

Oh be careful with that,
it's so delicate, it could easily break.

If you take it in your hands gently
you can hold it
close up to your eyes.

It's a bit hazy on the outside,
but if you wait for it to turn,
here and there you can see right through
and then you'll be really amazed!

Gently now, even though it looks solid enough,
you'd be surprised at just how flimsy it is.
Look there. Can you see the big blue bits?
I remember being so fascinated with them
that I wanted to touch them.

But you're not allowed to do that.
If you did, The High says you might damage it
because there's some protective coating
or gas or something surrounding the whole thing
and if that gets damaged, it could be serious.
What do you suppose the green bits are?

That's it, just let it rest in your palm.
Watch how it spins of its own accord.
Have you spotted the brown areas?
No, you mustn't touch the little white thing
going round it, The High says it's very important too,
a force or influence or balance perhaps.
Let's leave it now, careful, don't forget it's so very fragile.

It's name?
The High call it *Earth*.
Some say it's a sad place.

*John Rice*

## Pop Goes the Weasel!

Up and down the City Road,
   In and out the Eagle,
That's the way the money goes,
   Pop goes the weasel!

A ha'penny for a cotton ball,
　A farthing for a needle,
That's the way the money goes,
　Pop goes the weasel!

Half a pound of tuppenny rice,
　Half a pound of treacle,
Mix it up and make it nice,
　Pop goes the weasel!

Every time my mother goes out,
　The monkey's on the table,
Cracking nuts and eating spice,
　Pop goes the weasel!

If you want to buy a pig,
　Buy a pig with hairs on,
Every hair a penny a pair,
　Pop goes the weasel!

*Anon.*

# A Bedtime Rhyme for Young Fairies

One tired fairy,
Two folded wings,
Three magic wishes,
Four daisy rings,
Five moonlight dancers,
Six starlight spells,
Seven hidden treasures,
Eight silver bells,
Nine secret doorways,
Ten keys to keep,
And one little fairy
Fast asleep.

*Clare Bevan*

## *Us*

One, Dad;
Two, Mum;
Three, me;
Four, Tom.
Five, Gran;
Six, Gramp;
Seven, dog
Called Tramp.
Eight, cat
Called Puss;
No more,
That's Us.

*Eric Finney*

## *Blow, blow, thou winter wind*
(from *As You Like It*)

Blow, blow, thou winter wind,
Thou art not so unkind
  As man's ingratitude;
Thy tooth is not so keen,
Because thou art not seen,
  Although thy breath be rude.
Heigh-ho! sing, heigh-ho! unto the green holly:
Most friendship is feigning, most loving mere folly:
  Then, heigh-ho, the holly!
  This life is most jolly.

Freeze, freeze, thou bitter sky,
That dost not bite so nigh
  As benefits forgot:
Though thou the waters warp,
Thy sting is not so sharp
  As friends remember'd not.
Heigh-ho! sing, heigh-ho! unto the green holly:
Most friendship is feigning, most loving mere folly:
  Then, heigh-ho, the holly!
  This life is most jolly.

*William Shakespeare*

## Protection

I've got woollen underpants
By Jove, I'm glad I've got 'em
Cos when you toboggan and slide in the snow
You can get a very cold bottom

*Roger Stevens*

## Stairway to the Clouds

I took a stairway to the clouds
And a camel to the moon
A trampoline to Timbuktu
And a rocket to my room

A skateboard to the Red Sea
A submarine to Mars
A freight train to Atlantis
I dived up to the stars

Parachuting on the ocean
I rode my bike down deep
I took a racing car to bed
And drove myself to sleep

I caught a bus that flew
To a bridge across the seas
And then in my canoe
I slalomed through the trees

I scootered on thin ice
Space-hoppered into space
With ice skates on the running track
I raced the human race

I bounced upon my pogo stick
All round the equator
I scaled the peak of Everest
Thanks to an elevator

I rope-swung in the city
Piggybacked through town
Rode horses down the rivers
And skied deep underground

I swam across the deserts
And surfed on escalators
I roller-skated on glaciers
And leapfrogged high skyscrapers

I've travelled many places
In many different styles
Near and far and deep and wide
Millions of miles.

But no matter how I wander
No matter where I roam
Of all these special journeys
The best one is . . . back home.

*Paul Cookson*

# A Winter Night

It was a chilly winter's night;
   And frost was glitt'ring on the ground,
And evening stars were twinkling bright;
   And from the gloomy plain around
      Came no sound,
But where, within the wood-girt tow'r,
The churchbell slowly struck the hour;
As if that all of human birth
   Had risen to the final day,
And soaring from the wornout earth

Were called in hurry and dismay,
Far away;
And I alone of all mankind
Were left in loneliness behind.

*William Barnes*

## A Mocking Echo

*I am lost*
You are lost
*It's black as night*
You'll get a fright
*This is scary*
Really hairy
*Who is there?*
I'm a bear!
*Time to go*
You're too slow
*You're just an echo*
I don't think so!

*Catharine Boddy*

# December

## What's My Name?

I'm the sun that lights the playground before the work
  begins
I'm the smile when teacher cracks a joke
I'm the giggles and the grins
In assembly I'm the trophy that the winning team collects
In your maths book I'm the page of sums where every
  one's correct
I'm the pure blue sky and leafy green that wins the prize in
  art
I'm steamy, creamy custard dribbling down the cook's jam
  tart
I'm the noise of playtime rising through the stratosphere
I'm the act of kindness when you lent your kit to Mia
I'm the star you were awarded for your startling poetry
I'm the school gates swinging open on the stroke of half
  past three

If you look for me, you'll find me
What's my name?
Can you guess?
I live just round the corner and my name is happiness

*Roger Stevens*

## *Variation on An Old Rhyme*

This is the blackbird that wakes with a song.

This is the sun
That shines for the blackbird that wakes with a song.

This is the earth
That welcomes the sun
That shines for the blackbird that wakes with a song.

This is the snow that fell through the night
That covers the earth
That welcomes the sun
That shines for the blackbird that wakes with a song.

These are the children that cry with delight
That play in the snow that fell through the night
That covers the earth
That welcomes the sun
That shines for the blackbird that wakes with a song.

This is the wonderland of white
That surrounds the children that cry with delight
That play in the snow that fell through the night
That covers the earth
That welcomes the sun
That shines for the blackbird that wakes with a song.

This is the quarrel that started the fight
That stains the wonderland of white
That surrounds the children that cry with delight
That play in the snow that fell through the night
That covers the earth
That welcomes the sun
That shines for the blackbird that wakes with a song.

This is the wrong that none can put right
That caused the quarrel that started the fight
That stains the wonderland of white
That surrounds the children that cry with delight
That play in the snow that fell through the night
That covers the earth
That welcomes the sun
That shines for the blackbird that wakes with a song.

These are the nations in all their might
That suffer the wrong that none can put right
That caused the quarrel that started the fight
That stains the wonderland of white
That surrounds the children that cry with delight
That play in the snow that fell through the night
That covers the earth
That welcomes the sun
That shines for the blackbird that wakes with a song.

And this is the song that goes on in spite
Of all the nations in all their might
That suffer the wrong that none can put right
That causes the quarrels that start every fight
That stains the wonderland of white
That surrounds the children that cry with delight
That play in the snow that fell through the night
That covers the earth
That welcomes the sun
That shines just the same on everyone.

*John Mole*

3

## *Little Robin Redbreast*

Little Robin Redbreast
Sat upon a tree,
He sang merrily,
As merrily as could be.
He nodded with his head,
And his tail waggled he,
As little Robin Redbreast
Sat upon a tree.

*Anon.*

## *A Jolly Old Fellow in Red*

A jolly old fellow in red
set his reindeer on full speed ahead
and all in one night,
faster than light,
left presents round everyone's bed.

*Marian Swinger*

## *A Child's Calendar*

No visitors in January.
A snowman smokes a cold pipe in the yard.

They stand about like ancient women,
The February hills.
They have seen many a coming and going, the hills.

In March Moorfea is littered
With knock-kneed lambs.

Daffodils at the door in April,
Three shawled Marys.
A lark splurges in galilees of sky.

And in May
A russet stallion shoulders the hill apart.
The mares tremble.

The June bee
Bumps in the pane with a heavy bag of plunder.

Strangers swarm in July
With cameras, binoculars, bird books.

He thumped the crag in August,
A blind blue whale.

September crofts get wrecked in blond surges.
They struggle, the harvesters.
They drag loaf and ale-kirn into winter.

In October the fishmonger
Argues, pleads, threatens at the shore.

Nothing in November
But tinkers at the door, keening, with cans.

Some December midnight
Christ, lord, lie warm in our byre.
Here are stars, an ox, poverty enough.

*George Mackay Brown*

## Coronation

Bring him a garland of bright winter jasmine,
Twine a gold chaplet to circle his head,
Weave his crown softly now,
No thorn to harm his brow,
Wind it with kisses and small stars instead.

*Sue Cowling*

## Christmas Express

It's a perfect night for flying,
the moon is full and gold.
The stars shine out from darkest blue;
there are presents in the hold.

It's a perfect night for flying,
and the pilot's feeling jolly.
The cockpit's decked in tinsel
and mistletoe and holly.

It's a perfect night for flying.
The air is cold and bright.
We hurtle through the stratosphere –
we all enjoy the flight.

It's a perfect night for flying,
we're singing as we go.
We can hear a thousand voices
joining in from far below.

It's a perfect night for flying,
but the sky is broad and steep,
so when this reindeer's home, he'll spend
his Christmas Day asleep.

*Alison Chisholm*

# A Happy Christmas

I'm dreaming of a HAPPY Christmas
everybody has a HAPPY face
war draws to an end
and enemies become friends
Yeah! Love embraces
the human race.

*Levi Tafari*

# Christmas Glow

My house smells of Christmas:
pine resin, cinnamon,
gingerbread, cloves.

We've made mince pies
and fir-cone swags,
pomanders and mistletoe balls.
On the wall there's a spiced apple garland.
The fir tree greens the hall.
Red-berried holly and ivy tumble
over the open front door.

My house smells of Christmas:
pine resin, cinnamon,
gingerbread, cloves:

ready for the Star
and feathers of snow,
a newborn child,
myrrh, frankincense, gold:
to light my house
with that special, Christmas glow.

*Joan Poulson*

## Nativity Play

What will I be in the Christmas play?
Teacher's giving the parts out today.
Perhaps I'll be Joseph and look after Mary,
Or a shepherd who thinks that the angels are scary.
I'd like to be Herod, a villain so cruel,
Or the man with the stable whose inn was quite full.
Perhaps I'll be one of the three wise men.
Oh no! Oh no! I'm the donkey again.

*Alison Chisholm*

## There Was an Old Man of Dumbree

There was an Old Man of Dumbree,
Who taught little Owls to drink Tea;
For he said, 'To eat mice
Is not proper or nice,'
That amiable Man of Dumbree.

*Edward Lear*

# The Innkeeper's Story

I saw a baby in a manger.

I saw a baby in a manger
With two parents, Mary and Joseph.

I saw a baby in a manger
With two parents, Mary and Joseph,
And three wise kings
Who came on four camels.
(There was one to carry the presents.)

I saw a baby in a manger
With two parents, Mary and Joseph,
And three wise kings
With their four camels,
And five shepherds,
All dusty from the hills –
Oh yes, and they had six sheep with them.
(They couldn't leave them behind because of the wolves.)

I saw a baby in a manger
With two parents, Mary and Joseph,
And three wise kings
With their four camels,
And five shepherds,
With their six sheep
That couldn't be left behind,
And seven donkeys,
And eight cows . . .
Then there were the angels.

They kept flying around singing,
And it was hard to count them,
But there must have been at least nine.

Nine angels,
Eight cows,
Seven donkeys,
Six sheep,
Five shepherds,
Four camels,
Three wise kings,
Two parents,
A baby,

And one
Very special star.

*David Orme*

## *Winter Lights*

I fold myself
next to my window
and carefully watch
as the winter darkness
tucks itself slowly around me.

Outside,
cars are now giant cats
creeping slowly past
with their great yellow eyes
searching the way home.

In the distance
a train chatters towards me
pulling a necklace of lights
that sparkles along the railway track
until it is sucked into the dark.

*Ian Souter*

## Christmas Is Coming

Christmas is coming,
  The geese are getting fat,
Please to put a penny
  In the old man's hat.
If you haven't got a penny,
  A ha'penny will do;
If you haven't got a ha'penny,
  Then God bless you!

**Anon.**

## In the Bleak Mid-winter

In the bleak mid-winter
  Frosty wind made moan,
Earth stood hard as iron,
  Water like a stone;
Snow had fallen, snow on snow,
  Snow on snow,
In the bleak mid-winter
  Long ago.

Our God, Heaven cannot hold Him
  Nor earth sustain;
Heaven and earth shall flee away
  When he comes to reign:
In the bleak mid-winter
  A stable-place sufficed
The Lord God Almighty
  Jesus Christ.

Enough for Him, whom cherubim
  Worship night and day,
A breastful of milk
  And a mangerful of hay;
Enough for Him, whom angels
  Fall down before,
The ox and ass and camel
  Which adore.

Angels and archangels
  May have gathered there,
Cherubim and seraphim
  Thronged the air;
But only His mother
  In her maiden bliss
Worshipped the Beloved
  With a kiss.

What can I give Him,
  Poor as I am?
If I were a shepherd
  I would bring a lamb,
If I were a Wise Man
  I would do my part, –
Yet what I can I give Him,
  Give my heart.

*Christina Rossetti*

## *What Will They Give You?*

What will they give you,
my darling baby boy –
so early this dark morning?

> Will they give you seven candles
> to guide you through the night?

> Will they give you loaves and fishes
> and water sweet as wine?

> Will they give you a boat
> that can ride through the storm?

What will they give you,
my darling baby boy –
so early this dark morning?

> Will they give you a purse
> filled with silver gleaming bright?

> Will they give you a tree
> dressed in berries cold and white?

Will they give you a kiss
in a garden before dawn?

What will they give you,
my darling baby boy?

Will they give you
a crown of thorns?

*David Greygoose*

## A Christmas Blessing

God bless the master of this house,
   The mistress also,
And all the little children
   That round the table go;
And all your kin and kinsfolk,
   That dwell both far and near;
I wish you a Merry Christmas
   And a Happy New Year.

*Anon.*

## *All you that to feasting and mirth are inclined*

All you that to feasting and mirth are inclined,
Come here is good news for to pleasure your mind,
Old Christmas is come for to keep open house,
He scorns to be guilty of starving a mouse:
Then come, boys, and welcome for diet the chief,
Plum-pudding, goose, capon, minced pies, and roast beef.
The holly and ivy about the walls wind
And show that we ought to our neighbors be kind,
Inviting each other for pastime and sport,
And where we best fare, there we most do resort;
We fail not of victuals, and that of the chief,
Plum-pudding, goose, capon, minced pies, and roast beef.
All travellers, as they do pass on their way,
At gentlemen's halls are invited to stay,
Themselves to refresh, and their horses to rest,
Since that he must be Old Christmas's guest;
Nay, the poor shall not want, but have for relief,
Plum-pudding, goose, capon, minced pies, and roast beef.

*Anon.*

## *Light the Festive Candles*
### *(for Hanukkah)*

Light the first of eight tonight –
the farthest candle to the right.

Light the first and second too,
when tomorrow's day is through.

Then light three, and then light four –
every dusk one candle more

Till all eight burn bright and high,
honouring a day gone by

When the Temple was restored,
rescued from the Syrian lord,

And an eight-day feast proclaimed –
The Festival of Lights – well named

To celebrate the joyous day
when we regained the right to pray
to our one God in our own way.

*Aileen Fisher*

## *What the Donkey Saw*

No room in the inn, of course,
And not that much in the stable,
What with the shepherds, Magi, Mary,
Joseph, the heavenly host –
Not to mention the baby
Using our manger as a cot.
You couldn't have squeezed another cherub in
For love or money.

Still, in spite of the overcrowding,
I did my best to make them feel wanted.
I could see the baby and I
would be going places together.

U. A. Fanthorpe

## *Hanukkah*

Summoning the
sun
the Hanukkah lamp
glows
the miracle
reborn

*David Shalem*

## Red Boots On

Way down Geneva,
All along Vine,
Deeper than the snow drift
Love's eyes shine:

Mary Lou's walking
In the winter time.

She's got

*Red boots on, she's got*
*Red boots on,*
*Kicking up the winter*
*Till the winter's gone.*

So

Go by Ontario,
Look down Main,
If you can't find Mary Lou,
Come back again:

Sweet light burning
In winter's flame.

She's got

*Snow in her eyes, got*
*A tingle in her toes*
*And new red boots on*
*Wherever she goes*

So

All around Lake Street,
Up by St Paul,
Quicker than the white wind
Love takes all:

Mary Lou's walking
In the big snow fall.

*Red boots on, she's got*
*Red boots on,*
*Kicking up the winter*
*Till the winter's gone.*

*Kit Wright*

## *Love and Friendship*

Love is like the wild rose briar,
Friendship, like the holly tree
The holly is dark when the rose briar blooms,
But which will bloom most constantly?

The wild rose briar is sweet in spring,
Its summer blossoms scent the air
Yet wait till winter comes again
And who will call the wild-briar fair?

Then scorn the silly rose-wreath now
And deck thee with the holly's sheen
That when December blights thy brow
He still may leave thy garland green.

*Emily Brontë*

# A Visit from St Nicholas

'Twas the night before Christmas, when all through the
  house
Not a creature was stirring, not even a mouse;
The stockings were hung by the chimney with care,
In hopes that St Nicholas soon would be there;
The children were nestled all snug in their beds,
While visions of sugar-plums danced in their heads;
And mamma in her 'kerchief, and I in my cap,
Had just settled our brains for a long winter's nap –
When out on the lawn there arose such a clatter,
I sprang from my bed to see what was the matter.
Away to the window I flew like a flash,
Tore open the shutters, and threw up the sash.
The moon, on the breast of the new-fallen snow,
Gave the lustre of midday to objects below;
When, what to my wondering eyes should appear,
But a miniature sleigh and eight tiny reindeer,
With a little old driver, so lively and quick,
I knew in a moment it must be St Nick.
More rapid than eagles his coursers they came,
And he whistled, and shouted, and called them by name:
'Now, *Dasher*! now, *Dancer*! now, *Prancer* and *Vixen*!
On, *Comet*! on, *Cupid*! on, *Donder* and *Blitzen*!

To the top of the porch! to the top of the wall!
Now dash away! dash away! dash away all!'
As dry leaves that before the wild hurricane fly,
When they meet with an obstacle, mount to the sky;
So up to the house-top the coursers they flew
With the sleigh full of toys, and St Nicholas too.
And then, in a twinkling, I heard on the roof
The prancing and pawing of each little hoof –
As I drew in my head, and was turning around,
Down the chimney St Nicholas came with a bound.
He was dressed all in fur, from his head to his foot,
And his clothes were all tarnished with ashes and soot;
A bundle of toys he had flung on his back,
And he looked like a pedlar just opening his pack.
His eyes – how they twinkled; his dimples, how merry!
His cheeks were like roses, his nose like a cherry!
His droll little mouth was drawn up like a bow,
And the beard of his chin was as white as the snow;
The stump of a pipe he held tight in his teeth,
And the smoke it encircled his head like a wreath;
He had a broad face and a little round belly
That shook, when he laughed, like a bowl full of jelly.
He was chubby and plump, a right jolly old elf,
And I laughed when I saw him, in spite of myself;
A wink of his eye and a twist of his head
Soon gave me to know I had nothing to dread;
He spoke not a word, but went straight to his work,
And filled all the stockings; then turned with a jerk,
And laying his fingers aside of his nose,
And giving a nod, up the chimney he rose;

He sprang to his sleigh, to his team gave a whistle,
And away they all flew like the down of a thistle.
But I heard him exclaim, ere he drove out of sight,
'*Happy Christmas to all, and to all a good night!*'

*Clement Clarke Moore*

## The Sky Exploded

Night turned inside out
And suddenly was all ablaze
Across the blue-black sky
Like diamonds. It was day,
Like rainbows sparkling in salt spray,
Or waterfalls of light . . .
Not any sort of night
That anyone had ever seen before
   – or since.
The shepherds on the hill
screwed up their eyes against it
   – so bright it made them wince.
They heard the singing,
felt the wind of wild wings beating,
   – white and gleaming thunder
high in God's heaven.

All this.
All this fanfare-fuss, this mad amazing energy,
On this high hilltop,
This was not the main event.
That happened quietly behind the pub
In a shed they kept the donkey in.
There God was born
Not in a palace to be claimed by kings
Not in a rich man's house awash with *things*.
Not even underneath the angels' shining wings
But in a shed. With stuff.
For us. For ordinary us.

*Jan Dean*

## *Christmas Morning*

early on
everything frosted like iron
we woke, my brother and I,
to the creak on the stair
and silently
pumped up like balloons
with excitement
we pretended sleep
until Santa (or Mum or Dad)
had gone –

ducked our heads into Christmas
pillowsacks of –

crackly paper
oranges and apples sweet and tangy
chocolate money
plastic made-in-Hong-Kong rockets
sheriff's badge
pair of socks (from Auntie May, handknitted)
a colouring book
and pencils that smell of Friday afternoons in school
a bag of dinosaurs, red, blue, brown and green
a false nose
a set of magic tricks
a crêpe-paper cracker with glossy band
a rattly handful of walnuts at the bottom
a thread of cotton
a few sparks of glitter . . .

I wish I could live inside here
forever!

*Stephen Bowkett*

## *The Lost Pantomime*

Where's the pantomime?
It's behind you!
Oh no it isn't!
Oh yes it is!

*Nick Toczek*

## *Starfall*

Exploded stars,
cosmos swirled,
each winter fall
upon our world.

This dust of stars,
weightless, white,
drifts down and settles
in the night.

491

We wake to find
the fields aglow,
and wrongly call
this starfall . . . snow.

*Wes Magee*

## *Constant, Constant Little Light*

*A twenty-first-century version of Jane Taylor's poem 'The Star',
now universally known as the nursery rhyme 'Twinkle, twinkle
little star'*

Constant, constant little light,
catch my eye in darkest night.
What can speed so fast, so high,
laser like across the sky?

When the sleepy sun has set
and the night has cast her net.
It's then your orbit forms a ring,
round the earth a song to sing.

492

Constant, constant little light,
I know you're a satellite.

Cruising, spinning, seldom seen,
beaming pictures to our screens.
Weather-watching, tracking storms,
plotting maps and all life-forms.

Scanning, spying from above,
are you hawk or are you dove?
Silent, stealthy space age Thor,
armed with weapons for a real star war.

From your tiny, silver glow,
who can tell what wrongs may flow.
But for now I hold you bright,
constant, constant little light.

Constant, constant little light,
I know you're a satellite.

*John Rice*

## *Jack Frost*

Jack Frost,
Winter wizard
Brightens up the darkest night
Spells while we are fast asleep.

Jack Frost,
Winter jeweller
Encrusting spiders' webs with diamonds,
Icicle fingertips, silver breath.

Jack Frost,
Winter graffiti artist
Spray can magic, leaves his mark,
Christmas card scenery, the icing on the lake.

*Paul Cookson*

## *Almost New Year*

It's the last afternoon
of the old year
and already a full fat moon
is in charge of the sky.
It has nudged the sun
into a distant lake
and left it to drown,
while bare branch trees
like blackened fireworks
burst with sunset.
Frost is patterning the fields,
a tractor tries to furrow
the iron hard hill.
Winter's frown settles
on the face of the landscape.
It shrugs its shoulders,
gives in to January.

*Brian Moses*

# Index of First Lines

496

# Index of First Lines

# Index of First Lines

# Index of Poets

# Index of Poets

# Acknowledgements

The compiler and publisher would like to thank the following for permission to use copyright material:

**Jez Alborough**, 'A Smile', by permission of the author; **Geraldine Aldridge**, 'Tick Tock', by permission of the author; **Leo Aylen**, 'March Time: Dance Time', by permission of the author; **Chris Bambrough**, 'You Are Special', by permission of the author; **Bruce Barnes**, 'I Wrote Me a Poem', by permission of the author; **David Bateman**, 'Cross Your Fingers (For Luck)', by permission of the author; **Susan Bates**, 'Celebrations' and 'Ducking and Diving', by permission of the author'; **Gerard Benson**, 'Omba Bolomba' and 'Overheard on Safari', both from *Omba Bolomba: Poems by Gerard Benson*, Smith/Doorstop (2005), by permission of the author; **Clare Bevan**, 'A Bedtime Rhyme for Young Fairies' and 'Fairy Names', from *Fairy Poems* by Clare Bevan, Macmillan (2004), 'Monkey Motto', from *Join In . . . or Else*, ed. Nick Toczek, Macmillan (2000), 'Todd the Backyard King', from *The Works 5*, ed. Paul Cookson, Macmillan (2006), and 'The Three-headed Dog', all by permission of the author; **Valerie Bloom**, 'Haircut Rap', by permission of the author; **Catharine Boddy**, 'A Mocking Echo', by permission of the author; **Stephen Bowkett**, 'Christmas Morning' and 'The Shapeshifter's Riddle', both by permission of the author; **Philip Burton**, 'Caterpillar Salad Rap', from *Silly Poems*, ed. Paul Cookson, Scholastic (2006); **David Calder**, 'Lost' and 'This Is the Key to the Castle', both by permission of the author; **Richard Caley**, 'Working for the Master' and 'Ye Olde Pirate Drinking Song', both by permission of the author; **James Carter**, 'Electric Guitars', first published in *Cars Stars Electric Guitars*, Walker (2002), and 'Fuss Fuss Fuss', 'Take a Poem', 'What Will I Be When I Grow Up?', 'Where Did We Go?' and 'World of Weird', all by permission of the author; **Lisa Carter**, 'Sound Test', by permission of the author; **Debjani Chatterjee**, 'Mela Menagerie', first published in *Animal Antics* by Debjani Chatterjee, Pennine Press (2000), 'My Sari', first published in *Unzip Your Lips*, Macmillan (1998); **Alison Chisholm**, 'Christmas Express', first published in *The Big Book of Christmas*, Macmillan (2005), and 'Nativity Play', all by permission of the author; **Jane Clarke**, 'Are We There Yet?', 'Shadows' and 'Wrapping Tutankhamun', all by permission of the author; **John Clarke**, 'Earth Songs', by permission of the author; **John Coldwell**, 'Fish and Chips on Friday', by permission of the author; **Pie Corbett**, 'The Playground Monster', first published in *Rice, Pie and Moses* by John Rice, Pie Corbett and Brian Moses, Macmillan (1995); **Sue Cowling**, 'The Camel's Complaint', 'Coronation' and 'The Skin I'm In', all by permission of the author; **Jan Dean**, 'The Sky Exploded', by permission of the author; **Peter Dixon**, 'Lone Mission', 'Missing Important Things' and 'Muuuuuummmmmm', from *Weepers*

# Acknowledgements

by Peter Dixon, Peche Luna Books; **Rob Falconer,** 'George and the Dragon', by permission of the author; **U. A. Fanthorpe,** 'What the Donkey Saw', first published in *Christmas Poems* by U. A. Fanthorpe, Enitharmon & Peterloo (2002); **Eric Finney,** 'First Star' and 'Team Talk', first published in *Space Poems*, ed. Gaby Morgan, Macmillan (2006), 'Us', first published in *Family Poems* ed. Jennifer Curry, Scholastic (2002), all poems by permission of the author; **John Foster,** 'Shaun Short's Short Socks', from *Climb Aboard the Poetry Plane*, Oxford University Press (2000), and 'The Schoolkids' Rap' from *Word Wizard*, Oxford University Press (2001); **Katherine Gallagher,** 'Count-up to Planet Bed', first published in *Toothpaste Trouble*, Macmillan (2002); **Celia Gentles,** 'Ladybird', by permission of the author; **Martin Glynn,** 'At Dis Skool', 'Genius', 'I'm Proud to Be' and 'Wurd Up', all by permission of the author; **Judith Green,** 'A Message to My Sister', 'Playing Pooh-sticks with Trains', 'The Purple Llama Wishes You . . .', and 'Rhubarb Crumble', all by permission of the author; **Trevor Harvey,** 'What a Racket!', published in *Poetry Anthology*, ed. David Orme, Scholastic (1997), originally published in a longer version as 'Sounds Familiar' in *Performance Poems*, ed. Brian Moses, Southgate (1996); **John Hegley,** 'Body Poem', by permission of the author; **David Horner,** 'The Best Soundtrack Album in the World – Ever!', first published in *Cowboy – and Other Animals*, Apple Pie Publications (2005), and 'Cake Face', first published in *Body Noises*, Apple Pie Publications (1998); **Libby Houston,** 'Shop Chat', first published in *Tongue Twisters and Tonsil Twizzlers*, ed. Paul Cookson, Macmillan (1999); **Jean Kenward,** 'The Conversation', 'The Newcomer' and 'Tree and Leaf', all by permission of the author; **Ian Larmont,** 'Caterpillar', first published in *Join In . . . or Else*, Macmillan (2000), and 'Tick-tock', both by permission of the author; **Kevin McCann,** 'Counting Song' and 'Rain! Rain!', both by permission of the author; 'Watch Out, There's a Ghost About', first published in *Watch Out, There's a Ghost About*, OUP (2002); **Ian McMillan,** 'New Day' and 'This Little Poem', both by permission of the author; **Wes Magee,** 'Starfall' and 'What's Behind the Green Curtain', both by permission of the author; **Jane Mann,** 'I Dreamed Last Night', 'An Ace of Space' and 'Grandpa's Glasses', all by permission of the author; **Anthony Manville,** 'The Elephant', first published in *Whispering Trees*, Forward Press (2001), by permission of the author; **Gerda Mayer,** 'Barrel-Organ Song', originally 'Frantisek', and 'Old Mrs Lazibones', both first published in *The Knockabout Show* by Gerda Mayer, Chatto & Windus (1978), and 'There's a Bird That Comes Flying' (translated from a German folk song), first published in *Sheep Don't Go To School*, Bloodaxe (1999); **Robin Mellor,** 'Do It Yourself', by permission of the author; **Trevor Millum,** 'The Dark Avenger', 'Dick's Dog' and 'Song of the Homeworkers', all by permission of the author; **Tony Mitton,** 'Troll' and 'Voices of Water', both by permission of the author; **John Mole,** 'Variation on an Old Rhyme' and 'Wendy & Barry', both by permission of the author; **Michaela Morgan,** 'The Things Mums

# Acknowledgements

Say . . .', by permission of the author, and 'Question Time' from *Monster Poems* ed. John Foster, OUP; **Brian Moses,** 'Almost New Year' and 'Make Friends with a Tree', both by permission of the author; **Judith Nicholls,** 'Bodywork', first published in *Dragonsfire* by Judith Nicholls, Faber and Faber (1990), 'Christy's Rap' and 'In Praise of Aunties', all by permission of the author; **Grace Nichols,** 'Roller Skaters' (1994), reproduced with permission of Curtis Brown Group Ltd; **David Orme,** 'The Innkeeper's Story', by permission of the author; **Jack Ousbey,** 'Gran Can You Rap?', by permission of the author; **Gareth Owen,** 'The Commentator', 'Conversation Piece' and 'Don't Look Round!', all by permission of the author; **Brian Patten,** 'A Small Dragon', reprinted from *Collected Love Poems*, Harper Perennial, 'The Cook's Tragedy' and 'Embryonic Mega-Stars', all by permission of the author c/o Rogers, Coleridge & White; **Noel Petty,** 'What For!', by permission of the author; **Gervase Phinn,** 'Creative Writing', first published in *Don't Tell the Teacher*, by Gervase Phinn, Puffin (2006); **Tim Pointon,** 'Railway Stations', by permission of the author; **Joan Poulson,** 'Christmas Glow', by permission of the author; **Phil Rampton,** 'Garden Rhyme', by permission of the author; **James Reeves,** 'Things to Remember', by permission of the James Reeves Estate; **John Rice,** 'Leisure Centre, Pleasure Centre', from *Rockets and Quasars*, Aten Press (1984), 'Constant, Constant Little Light', from *The Upside Down Frown*, ed. Andrew Fusek Peters, Wayland (1999), 'Castle to be Built in the Woods', from *The Works 3*, ed. Paul Cookson, Macmillan (2004), 'Careful With That, You Might Break It', from *The Works 5*, ed. Paul Cookson, Macmillan (2006), 'Seaside Song', from *Zoomballoomballistic*, Aten Press (1982); **Coral Rumble,** 'The First Bit', first published in *The Rhyme Riot*, ed. Gaby Morgan, Macmillan (2003); **Jane Saddler,** 'Run', by permission of the author; **Darren Sardelli,** 'My Locker'and 'The Fastest Kid in School', both by permission of the author; **Vernon Scannell,** 'My Dog' and 'I Bit an Apple', both by permission of the author; **Robert Scotellaro,** 'Pow!-erful Sound Effects', by permission of the author; **Fred Sedgwick,** 'The Cat from Down the Road', first published in *Pizza, Curry, Fish and Chips* by Fred Sedgwick, Longman (1994); **Andy Seed,** 'Cloakroom Argument', by permission of the author; **Andrea Shavick,** 'How to Successfully Persuade . . .', first published in *Unzip Your Lips Again*, ed. Paul Cookson, Macmillan (1999); **Ron Simmons,** 'Storms', by permission of the author; **Ian Souter,** 'Baby Rap', 'That's You and Me!' and 'Winter Lights', all by permission of the author; **Roger Stevens,** 'James Bond Car', 'Julius Caesar's Last Breakfast' and 'Poem for Sale', from *I Did Not Eat the Goldfish* by Roger Stevens, Macmillan (2002), 'Louder', from *Never Trust a Lemon* by Roger Stevens, Rabbit Press (1995), 'The Most Important Rap', from *Performance Poems*, ed. Brian Moses, Southgate (1996), 'Farewell, Pete', 'The Millennium Falcon', 'Nineteen Things to Do in Winter', 'Protection' and 'Whoops!', all from *Why Otters Don't Wear Socks* by Roger Stevens, Macmillan (2007), 'Let Me Hear You Say', 'Poem for Attracting

# Acknowledgements

Mum's Attention' and 'What's My Name?', all by permission of the author; **Marian Swinger**, 'A Jolly Old Fellow in Red', by permission of the author'; **Lynne Taylor**, 'Spring', by permission of the author; **Charles Thomson**, 'I've Never Seen', by permission of the author; **Angela Topping**, 'Carnival' and 'Dear Spiders', both by permission of the author; **Jill Townsend**, 'Tornado', first published in *The Elements in Poetry: Air*, ed. Andrew Fusek Peters, Evans Brothers (2006), and 'Going to the Olympics', both by permission of the author; **Steve Turner**, 'Hard to Please' and 'Why Are You Late for School?', both from *Dad, You're Not Funny*, Lion Publishing (1999); 'I Like Words' and 'The Jumping Game', both from *The Day I Fell Down The Toilet*, Lion Publishing (1996); **Kaye Umansky**, 'The Horrible House on Haunted Hill', 'A Plate of Potatoes' and 'Who's Baddest?', reproduced by permission of the author, c/o Caroline Sheldon Literary Agency; **Barrie Wade**, 'Unfinished Poem', by permission of the author; **Dave Ward**, 'Kidding Around' and 'When It's All Over', both by permission of the author; **Lisa Watkinson**, 'Parents' Jobs', by permission of the author; **Clive Webster**, 'Me and You' and 'Transported to Australia', both by permission of the author; **Linda Lee Welch**, 'Winter Song', first published in *Poetry Works*, Folens, and 'Move it', both by permission of the author; **Colin West**, 'Christine Crump' and 'Socks', both by permission of the author; **John Whitworth**, 'Halloween Poem', by permission of the author; **Kate Williams**, 'City Centre Saturday', by permission of the author; **Kit Wright**, 'Red Boots On', by permission of the author; **Bernard Young**, 'Lady Lollipop', from *Wanted Alive*, Hands Up Books (2004); **Benjamin Zephaniah**, 'Body Talk', first published in *Talking Turkeys* by Benjamin Zephaniah, Puffin Books.

Every effort has been made to trace the copyright holders, but if any have been inadvertently overlooked then the publishers will be pleased to make the necessary arrangement at the first opportunity.

# Every kind of poem you will ever need for Key Stage 2

## Chosen by Pie Corbett

A fantastic book of poems for Years 3, 4, 5 and 6. Contains poems which cover every form and theme of the Literacy Strategy, an index of poem types, advice for reading and writing poems, lots of poetry activities and some workshop ideas and lesson plans.

A must-have for teachers!

# A Poet a Week

## Chosen by Paul Cookson

52 poets and 364 of the best poems of all time.
This contains a huge variety of forms and styles and all
manner of subject matter.

There are ballads, riddles, tongue-twisters, sonnets, shape
poems, raps, narrative verses and haikus; it contains poems
about seasons, festivals, animals, love, war, life and death,
food and football, to name a few. There is also a biography
of each poet at the beginning of his or her week.

An essential book for teachers, but also a joyful
celebration of poets and poetry that readers will return
to again and again.

# THE WORKS 4

Every kind of poem on every
topic that you will ever need
for the Literacy Hour

## Chosen by Pie Corbett and Gaby Morgan

Divided into 26 alphabetical sections
featuring poems relevant to the Literacy Hour.

The Ark and other creatures, Boys' stuff, Celebrations
and festivals, Dinosaurs, dragons and dodos, Elements,
seasons and the natural world, Friends and families, Girls'
stuff, Home life, Impossible and incredible, Journeys,
Kissing and other things best avoided, Love, death, war
and peace, Monsters, ghouls and ghosts, Nonsense,
Ourselves and others, People and places, Queens, kings and
historical stuff, Rescuing the world, Senses and feelings,
Teachers, Unpleasant things, Viewpoints, Wonder,
X-words and wordplay, Young and old, Zapping aliens.

**THE WORKS 5**

Every kind of poem, from an alphabet of poets, that you will ever need for the Literacy Hour

## Chosen by Paul Cookson

Contains 260 poems from 260 poets:

John Agard, Allan Ahlberg, John Betjeman, Lewis Carroll, Paul Cookson, Emily Dickinson, Carol Ann Duffy, T. S. Eliot, Eleanor Farjeon, John Foster, David Harmer, Seamus Heaney, Jenny Joseph, John Keats, Edward Lear, Roger McGough, Brian Moses, Grace Nichols, Wilfred Owen, Brian Patten, Michael Rosen, William Shakespeare, Kaye Umansky, Oscar Wilde, W. B. Yeats and Benjamin Zephaniah, to name just a handful.

# THE WORKS 6

Every kind of poem you will
ever need for assembly.

## Chosen by Pie Corbett

From poems about faith, the environment, happiness and
friendship to poems about loss and conflict. There are
poems to celebrate achievement and poems to help us
deal with the times we live in.

A book packed with gems for dipping into
time and time again.

# A selected list of titles available from Macmillan Children's Books

The prices shown below are correct at the time of going to press. However, Macmillan Publishers reserves the right to show new retail prices on covers, which may differ from those previously advertised.

| | | |
|---|---|---|
| **Read Me 1** | 978-0-330-37353-1 | £6.99 |
| **Read Me 2** | 978-0-330-39132-0 | £6.99 |
| **Read Me and Laugh** | 978-0-330-43557-4 | £6.99 |
| **The Works** | 978-0-330-48104-5 | £6.99 |
| **The Works 2** | 978-0-330-39902-9 | £6.99 |
| **The Works 3** | 978-0-330-41578-1 | £6.99 |
| **The Works 4** | 978-0-330-43644-1 | £6.99 |
| **The Works 5** | 978-0-330-39870-1 | £5.99 |
| **The Works 6** | 978-0-330-43439-3 | £6.99 |
| **The Works 7** | 978-0-330-44424-8 | £6.99 |
| **The Works 8** | 978-0-330-46407-9 | £7.99 |
| **The Works Key Stage 1** | 978-0-330-43947-3 | £5.99 |
| **The Works Key Stage 2** | 978-0-330-43949-7 | £5.99 |

All Pan Macmillan titles can be ordered from our website, www.panmacmillan.com, or from your local bookshop and are also available by post from:

**Bookpost, PO Box 29, Douglas, Isle of Man IM99 1BQ**
Credit cards accepted. For details:
Telephone: 01624 677237
Fax: 01624 670923
Email: bookshop@enterprise.net
www.bookpost.co.uk

**Free postage and packing in the United Kingdom**